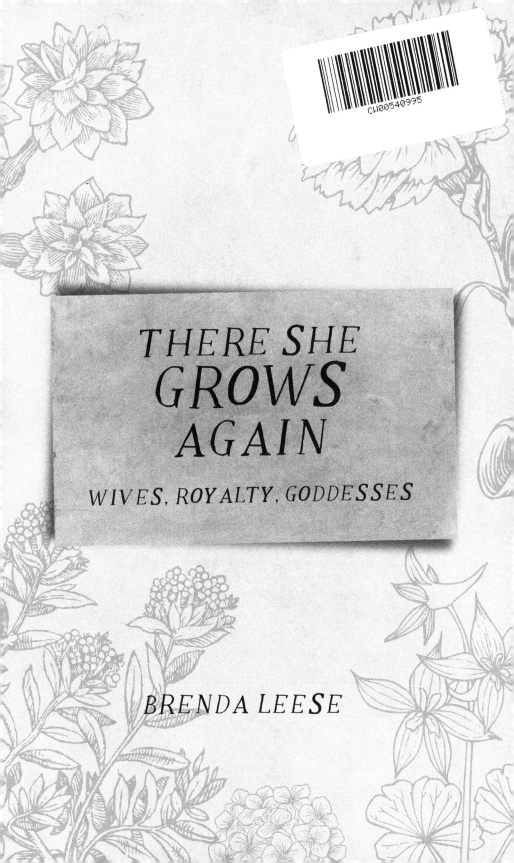

THERE SHE GROWS AGAIN

WIVES, ROYALTY, GODDESSES

BRENDA LEESE

Published in 2023 by Brenda Leese

www.florafeatures.co.uk

ISBN: 978-1-913898-38-0

Book Design by Russell Holden
www.pixeltweakspublications.com

Pixel Tweaks Publications
SELF PUBLISHING MADE SIMPLE

Cover illustration © Sophie Holme

Printed by Ingram

There She Grows Again
Women In Plant Names
WIVES, ROYALTY, GODDESSES

BY THE AUTHOR BRENDA LEESE

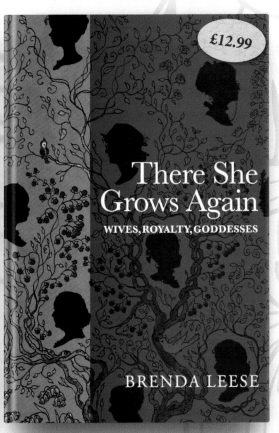

£12.99

This is the second book about the lives of women who have had a plant or plants named after them in the form of a genus or species. The book aims to highlight the contribution made by women to botanical science, where they have been so often overshadowed by men. It details the lives of 16 women who were the wives of well-known plantsmen, 10 members of various royal families and 13 goddesses. For each, there is a short biography including details of why they were chosen to have a plant named after them, followed by information about their plants. The first book, There She Grows, published in 2018 began the story by outlining the lives of 34 'Plants-women', who were either botanists, horticulturalists, plant collectors or botanical artists in their own right.

This book is a wonderful gem which tells the stories of a wide range of women who have been immortalised in plant names. Some of the plants will be familiar to you, others less so. I found this book very informative and full of delightful surprises with plenty of background information and useful sources.

Advolly Richmond
Garden writer, historian and a television presenter, who regularly appears on BBC's *Gardeners' World.*

Paperback: 200 pages
Publisher: Brenda Leese
Language: English
ISBN-13: 978-1-913898-38-0
Product Dimensions: 15.2 x 1 x 22.9 cm
For more details contact the author at: florafeatures@gmail.com

Flora Features
www.florafeatures.co.uk

Pixel Tweaks Publications
SELF PUBLISHING MADE SIMPLE
WWW.PIXELTWEAKSPUBLICATIONS.COM

For Mary again!

'So often people get forgotten in history, usually woman whose identities start to fade as soon as they had adopted their married name. This book is a wonderful gem which tells the stories of a wide range of women who have been immortalised in plant names. Some of the plants will be familiar to you, others less so. I found this book very informative and full of delightful surprises with plenty of background information and useful sources. Enjoy a glimpse into the lives of these women who would no doubt be pleasantly surprised if not amused, to be remembered through the plants in our gardens.'

Advolly Richmond
Garden writer, historian and a television presenter, who regularly appears on BBC's *Gardeners' World*.

PREFACE

As a child growing up in the 1950s, I lived on the edge of the city – a city only by virtue of having an impressive hill top cathedral – in an area surrounded by disused gravel pits and meadows full of wild flowers – all now submerged by housing and industrial estates of course. It was here that my first interest in wild flowers developed, though I had no idea at that time that the study of plants was called botany. However, I was encouraged by my parents and won a pressed flower competition at my school by submitting just one of the three booklets of flowers I had collected. I still have them! Collecting wild flowers would be very unusual nowadays, but at the time was something that many people did.

My interest persisted, encouraged by teachers at my school, and I went on to do an undergraduate degree in botany and biochemistry at London University followed by a DPhil at the University of York where I wrote my thesis on chloroplast structure and development in maize (*Zea mays*) leaves.

Ultimately, I became an academic researcher, not in botany but in health sciences (a long story!) but the processes involved in doing research in different subject areas are similar: so, I knew how to conduct a research project, search the literature critically and put the whole thing together as a coherent story – more or less! However, despite getting side-tracked into health sciences for around 30 years my love of botany was undimmed. All I needed was the opportunity, incentive and most importantly, a theme.

All three came about when I decided to enrol on a three-year BTEC course in horticulture at a local college. The course required a project, so here I had both opportunity and incentive and most importantly, a deadline.

So where did the idea for this book begin? It had been in the back of my mind for some years! I was aware that books about plant hunters rarely featured women, and that male plant hunters often had plants named after them. What about those plants named after women? Why was it that their lives rarely featured in books about plant discoveries? Perhaps there was no story to tell? I therefore decided to write my BTEC project on the lives of women who did have plants named after them. I soon found that there were, indeed, many such women but that their life stories were less likely to be written about than the corresponding lives of men. This book, and my earlier book *There She Grows*, therefore, concern the biographies of these pioneering women accompanied by descriptions of their wonderful plants. I decided early on to focus on genus and species names rather than cultivars. Cultivar names are used in horticulture but as a botanist by background I wanted to concentrate on plants that are found in the wild. The naming of plants is complex and still evolving, so for the women in these books to have been immortalised in a plant name or names is quite an achievement and they deserve to be more widely known. This book, and my previous one, *There She Grows*, are small steps in that direction.

The book begins with an introduction setting the scene for the world in which these women lived, including a section on the naming of plants and how their names are constantly changing. Chapter 2 provides details of the life stories of 'wives', Chapter 3 of 'royalty', Chapter 4 of 'goddesses' and the final chapter presents a summary of the findings.

CONTENTS

INTRODUCTION

INTRODUCTION

This is the second book about the lives of women who have had a plant or plants named after them in the form of a genus or species. The first book, *There She Grows*, published in 2018 outlined the lives of 34 'Plants-women'; - those who were either botanists, horticulturalists, plant collectors or botanical artists in their own right.[1] This book continues the story by detailing the lives of those women who were either the wives of plant hunters, royalty or goddesses in mythology.

Ideally this book should stand on its own without anyone having first to read *There She Grows*, though I hope you will, of course! This means that there is some repetition, which can simply be passed over by anyone who has already read *There She Grows*. In particular the section on The Beginning is needed for both books, together with some new tables in Chapter One and the Summary of the Findings. I have not repeated the historical background since this is most relevant to the women in *There She Grows*; however, an additional section is provided here on how plants are named, with details about the naming of plants after royalty and goddesses given in the relevant chapters.

At this point I should also make it clear that the paper on which this book is printed is not the usual white. The off-white colour is intended to represent an older Victorian publication and the brown blocks containing the plant details are representative of labels used by the early botanists. An 'anomaly' specific to this second book is the question whether goddesses can be regarded as 'women'? Perhaps not, but here I shall continue to refer to them in this manner for ease of writing. Further, in *There She Grows* I was able to use books and journals as sources of information but for this second volume, little is available from such sources and I have had to rely much more on the internet, as can be seen from the list of references at the end of each chapter.

The Beginning

As noted in *There She Grows*, the initial problem was where to begin. Although books about male plant hunters are relatively common, those featuring women much less so.[2-5] What would be the best way of identifying plants named after women? Out of several books that list the derivation of plant names, I decided to select the *A to Z of Plant Names* by Allen J. Coombes[6] which lists plants alphabetically by genus together with the species associated with that genus, as well as the origin of the names. After identification, the female names were allocated to one of four groups, namely plants-women, wives, royalty and goddesses. This method of selection provided many women's names but gave no indication of what proportion of women giving their names to plants was represented. It feels rather like being on the edge of a pit and not knowing how deep it is! Coombes states only that his book provides '...*names of the more commonly grown plants*', but provides no further details.[6] There are approximately 352,000 species of angiosperms (flowering plants), approximately 16,000 genera and 620 families.[7] However, these numbers are approximations since new species continue to be added and names are frequently changed. For example, there is an online list of 175 cacti named after women, plus a further similarly sized list of succulents.[8] The women profiled in this book therefore most likely represent a small sample only of those recognised in plant names but whose biographies provide a fascinating insight into their lives.

Summary of Findings

The women identified from Coombes can be divided into four distinct groups.[6] The first comprises women who were themselves plant hunters and went on expeditions overseas, who went to live overseas or who went plant hunting near where they were living. They were either plant hunters themselves or botanical artists, botanists or horticulturalists, and sometimes more than one of these. For simplicity, and a lack of any other suitable definition I have designated this group as 'Plants-women' in the broadest sense of the term; - to *mean women who have some special knowledge about plants*. Many of the women in this group had no formal botanical or horticultural training yet were able to create a significant niche for themselves. They were the subject of *There She Grows*, and numbered 34. This second book covers groups 2, 3 and 4. Group 2 comprises the wives of male plant hunters, with plants found by or named after them, usually by their husbands. The third group includes members of royal families and the fourth are goddesses in mythology. The numbers in the four groups are as follows:

Plants-women	n=34 (the subjects of *There She Grows*)
Wives	n=16
Royalty	n=10
Goddesses	n=13
TOTAL	n=73

There are 39 individuals named in this book; 16 wives, 10 royalty and 13 goddesses. Table 1.1 lists the 16 wives in order of their date of birth, together with the plants named after them. Each has a single plant except for Lucile Boissier, Ellen Ganderton Wilson, Mrs Benson and Juliana Schneider, who each have two. This means that the 16 wives have 20 plants described here. The birth and death dates are not known for 5 (31%) of them, and Mrs Benson's first name has not been found. Their plants include three from each of the families Rosaceae, Orchidaceae and Liliaceae and two each from the Berberidaceae and Bromeliaceae families. Table 1.2 gives similar information for the royalty featured in the book, with a diversity of plant families. Each of the 10 members of the royalty is represented by a single plant except for Queen Victoria who has two, making 11 plants in total. The dates of one of the women are not given since whether she was the person associated with the plant is disputed. The 13 goddesses and their plants are listed in Table 1.3 without dates. Five (36%) of the 13 plants are from the Orchidaceae family. Overall, 8 (19%) of the 42 plants are orchids, the largest group.

Table 1.1: Wives and their Plants

Name	Plant	Family	Dates
Dorothea Banks	*Rosa banksiae*	Rosaceae	1758-1828
Jane Franklin	*Acradenia frankliniae*	Rutaceae	1791-1828
Lucile Boissier	*Ompholodes luciliae*	Boraginaceae	1822-1849
	Chionodoxa luciliae	Liliaceae	
Eleanor Carmichael Aitchison	*Rosa ecae*	Rosaceae	1845-1897
Edith Blake	*Bauhinia blakeana*	Fabaceae	1845-1926
Elizabeth Lawrence	*Aerides lawrenceae*	Orchidaceae	1845-1916
Mary Allen Sargent	*Lilium sargentiae*	Liliaceae	1853-1919
Ellen Ganderton Wilson	*Berberis wilsoniae*	Berberidaceae	1872-1930
	Rosa helenae	Rosaceae	
Florinda Kingdon-Ward	*Primula florindae*	Primulaceae	1896-1972
Eva Racine Sarasy Foster	*Aechmea racinae*	Bromeliaceae	1910-1991
Jean Macklin	*Lilium mackliniae*	Liliaceae	1921-2011
Mrs Benson	*Thunia bensoniae*	Orchidaceae	-
	Dendrobium bensoniae	Orchidaceae	-
Martha Erni	*Lithops marthae*	Aizoaceae	-
Catherine Pancratia Maurandy	*Maurandya scandens*	Plantaginaceae	-
Carolina Morren	*Neoregelia carolinae*	Bromeliaceae	-
Juliana Schneider	*Berberis julianae*	Berberidaceae	-
	Syringa julianae	Oleaceae	-

Table 1.2: Royalty and their Plants

Name	Plant	Family	Dates
Queen Zenobia	*Zenobia speciosa*	Ericaceae	240-274
Queen Charlotte	*Strelitzia reginae*	Strelitziaceae	1744-1818
Queen Maria Luisa	*Aloysia citrodora*	Verbernaceae	1751-1819
Empress Josephine	*Lapageria rosea*	Philesiaceae	1763-1814
Queen Anna Paulowna	*Paulownia tomentosa*	Scrophulariaceae	1795-1865
Countess von Hardenberg	*Hardenbergia violacea*	Fabaceae	1814-1871
Queen Victoria	*Agave Victoria-reginae*	Agavaceae	1819-1901
	Victoria amazonica	Nymphaecaeae	
Queen Alexandra	*Rheum alexandre*	Polygonaceae	1844-1925
Queen Natalie	*Ramonda nathaliae*	Gesneriaceae	1859-1941
Hortense van Nassau	*Hydrangea hortensia*	Hydrangeaceae	-

Table 1.3: Goddesses and their Plants

Name	Plant	Family
Artemis	*Artemisia ludoviciana*	Asteraceae
Aspasia	*Aspasia epidendroides*	Orchidaceae
Cassiopeia	*Cassiope mertensiana*	Ericaceae
Danae	*Danae racemosa*	Asparagaceae
Diana	*Dianella ensifolia*	Asparagaceae
Dryads	*Dryas octopetala*	Rosaceae
Hebe	*Hebe speciosa*	Plantaginaceae
Laelia	*Laelia grandiflora*	Orchidaceae
Leucothea	*Leucothoe axillaris*	Ericaceae
Lycaste	*Lycaste cruenta*	Orchidaceae
Pandora	*Pandorea jasminoides*	Bignoniaceae
Pleione	*Pleione limprichtii*	Orchidaceae
Promeneia	*Promenaea xanthina*	Orchidaceae

Plant Hunting

The late 18th and 19th centuries were times of great exploration with the expansion of the British Empire, when many exotic plants were brought back to Britain for the first time.[3] Kew Gardens, established in 1759, became prominent as the foremost botanic garden in the world.[9] Until then, plant hunting had been the preserve of private individuals, associations and academic societies but now botanic gardens, and later, commercial nurseries (e.g. Veitch) began to sponsor plant hunters in order to increase their stock of exotic plants.[9] Botanic gardens were set up throughout the British Empire, including Calcutta (1787), Sydney (1816) and Colombo (1821). Britain was not alone; France, for example, was equally interested in botanical exploration. The Jardin du Roi was established in Paris between 1626 and 1640, later being known as the Jardin des Plantes. It received plants from the French colonies, with the Empress Josephine an enthusiast.[9] In early 19th century England, botanic gardens were set up in cities and towns including Liverpool (1836), Sheffield (1836), Birmingham (1832) and Chiswick (1821).[5] By the 1840s Kew began to publish colonial flora.[9] The scope for naming new plants was immense but was mainly undertaken by men.

The Naming of Plants

Horticulturalists and botanists are well aware that plant names do not always stay the same with some changes seeming perverse and inexplicable, as well as unwanted. Before considering why plant names change it is useful to examine how they are named in the first place. Classification or taxonomy as it is termed, is a fundamental requirement for understanding the structure of the world. Where would chemists be without the Periodic Table of the Elements, or meteorologists without windspeed tables? Botanists are no different. In the context of this book, taxonomy puts different plants into groups with similar characteristics to help scientists and others to make sense of their world. For this to be done, plant groups obviously need names.

Plant names are now well documented and regulated but this was not always the case. A question that many ask about the plant hunters of the 18th and 19th centuries is: how did they know whether the plants they found on their expeditions had already been named? The answer is, probably: they didn't! However, many were experts in plant identification, typically of specific families or genera, and took with them the reference books available at that time.[10] Nevertheless, plants were sometimes named more than once and had to be renamed when the duplication became known.[3] Frequently, plant hunters would send their finds to Kew, or other botanical gardens, for verification and authentication of their names.

Names need to be unique in order to aid communication and avoid confusion. Common names of plants have varied historically, especially from area to area.

CARL LINNAEUS

An example is *Galium aparine*, known variously as goosegrass, cleavers, bedstraw, stickyweed, sticky willy etc. depending on the geographical location. Another example is the bluebell. In England the plant known as the bluebell is *Hyacinthoides non-scripa* but it has 20 other common names and to confuse matters further the bluebell of Scotland is the harebell of England – *Campanula rotundi-*

folia. Plants were also named in various languages, adding to the problem. The situation became so fraught that rules for the naming of plants had to be introduced. Step forward Carl Linnaeus (1707-1778) who is credited with starting this process.[11]

Carl Linnaeus was born in Southern Sweden and spent most of his life at Uppsala University where he was Professor of Botany and Medicine. He is the most famous of all Swedish scientists and his life and achievements have been much written about.[12-15] He is probably rightly named the '*Father of Plant Taxonomy*'. His main achievement, leaving aside his classification system, was in developing the binomial system of plant names which is still in use today.[11] His genius lay in bringing together the findings of earlier botanists into one over-riding concept with wide applicability. Before Linnaeus, well-known historical figures such as Aristotle, Theophrastus and Pliny had written about the classification of plants, but mainly in terms of their medicinal qualities. Later, various botanists had defined the basis of the binomial system (G. Bauhin 1560-1625); the plant

THE LINNAEUS GARDEN IN UPPSALA

family (Magnol 1638-1715); the genus (Tournefort 1656-1708) and the species (Ray 1627-1705); but plants were still described in terms of polynomials or Latin phrases.

In his volume '*Species Plantarum*' (1753) Linnaeus also used this system but added a single word, which, combined with the genus, gave rise to a binomial (genus followed by species).[16] This solved the three problems: (i) polynomials consisting of lengthy and unwieldy names based on their description, (ii) differing local names for the same plant and (iii) names in different languages – from now on it had to be Latin. After Linnaeus, plant taxonomy continued to evolve, notably with the inclusion of a greater number of observ-

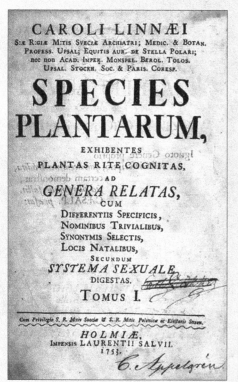

SPECIES PLANTARUM TITLE PAGE

EXAMPLE PAGE FROM SPECIES PLANTARUM

able characteristics. Plant classification has continued to develop and is currently undergoing further change based on DNA sequencing, but it was Linnaeus who set the whole process in motion.

The importance of having a name for a plant that is understood worldwide was brought

PAGE FROM THE CHINESE FLOWER BOOK

home to me on a botanical tour to Yunnan, China in 2017. A book of local plants with the title in English '*The Wild Ornamental Plants in the Three Parallel Rivers*' was written entirely in Chinese - (except for the title).[17] It contained pictures and descriptions of many of the plants we found on our plant hunting excursions, as well as the names of the plants: the key to using the book. The descriptions did not matter as they could be found elsewhere, whereas having the worldwide botanical name of the plant in Latin made the book useable by all, whatever their native language.

Naming Wild Plants

The next move in rules for naming plants took place with the adoption of the International Code of Botanical Nomenclature at a meeting of the Botanical Congress in Vienna in 1905.[18] The name of the Code survived until 2011 when it was changed to The International Code of Nomenclature for algae, fungi, and plants (ICN) at the International Botanical Congress in Melbourne.[19] It is frequently referred to as the Botanical Code and is administered by the International Association for Plant Taxonomy (IAPT). It is now reviewed every six years, most recently at the Botanical Congress in Shenzhen, China in 2017 [20] with the next due in Rio de Janeiro in 2023. One important aspect of the Code is the *'application of the principle of priority'*. That is, the first *published* name given to a plant has absolute priority.[21] The person providing the description is known as the Authority and their name (or abbreviation) is added to the plant binomial name in official documents; for example, the plant *Acradenia frankliniae Kippist.* (Wirewood) was described in 1852 by Richard Kippist (1812-1882), an English botanist. The 2011 congress in Melbourne removed the requirement for a description of a new species to be in Latin as had been the custom until then, and allowed official descriptions in online only journals. This decision had, however, no effect on the plant name which has still to be in Latin. There is a separate code, the International Code of Nomenclature for Cultivated Plants, first introduced in 1953, which sets requirements for all new cultivar names.[22] The most recent edition (No.9) was published in 2016. Since cultivars or cultivated varieties are not included in this book no further mention of them will be given.

Plant Name Changes

Types of name changes
Name changes can be nomenclatural, taxonomic or genetic.

1). Nomenclatural: At the height of plant exploration in the 19th century, plant names had become confused, with different names being given to the same plants. This problem was solved by the International Botanical Code (ICN), described above, which stated that the earliest published name was the one that should be used.[18]

Later published names which might be in common usage became synonyms. If an earlier description of a plant is found at any time, then this is the one that must be used.

2). Taxonomic: These changes can be much more contentious and argued over by botanists until a consensus is reached. Botanists may spend much of their working lives on a specific genus or plant family in order to investigate relationships using techniques such as light and electron microscopy, herbaria (pressed dried plants), and more recently, genetics. As a result, genera or families may be split or combined and then published as revisions. The Botanical Congresses are where botanists can debate the changes they would like to see. These debates can become quite heated when those for and against changes state their case.[23]

3). Genetic: It was in the early 1990s that developments in genetics, combined with improvements in computation, allowed the detailed analysis of plant genomes. DNA analysis data allowed botanists to determine in much more detail the relationships between plant families, resulting in some reclassifications, though in general, the new findings did not differ as much as might have been expected from those based on visual characteristics. It took a few years for scientists to become sufficiently confident of their results to develop a revised classification system. Eventually groups of scientists got together and developed the new system which they termed the Angiosperm Phylogeny Group classification (APG), first published in 1998, followed by three further versions, the latest (APG1V) being in 2016.[24] With each version, fewer anomalies have been recorded giving botanical gardens, herbaria and other organisations the confidence to reorganise their classification systems along APG lines.

The search for new plants continues. For example, in 2020 it was reported that Kew scientists had discovered 156 new species of flowering plants and fungi.[25] It has been estimated there are up to 100,000 species of undiscovered flowering plants globally, some of which may be of economic importance, so the search goes on. Global warming will most likely have an impact on plants and many may become extinct. Kew scientists maintain the seed bank at Wakehurst Place in order to preserve as many species as possible for future generations. As long as there are new plants waiting to be discovered the work of the botanists involved in genetic analyses will be vital in understanding the relationships between plants and with their environment, ensuring they receive appropriate names which are not duplicated elsewhere.

The remainder of this book is divided into four chapters each of which features a short introduction. Chapter 2 describes the lives of sixteen women who have had a plant named after them by virtue of having a husband known for his botanical interests. Chapter 3 considers the lives of ten members of various royal families and Chapter 4 chronicles thirteen women in mainly Greek mythology. The final Chapter summarises the findings.

References

1. Leese, B. *There She Grows*, Pixel Tweaks Publications, Ulverston, 2018.

2. Hyams, E. *The Story of England's Flora*. Kestrel Books, England, 1979.

3. Campbell-Culver, M. *The Origin of Plants*. Random House, London, 2001.

4. Gribbin, M. & Gribbin, J. *Flower Hunters*. Oxford University Press, Oxford, 2008.

5. Short, P. *In Pursuit of Plants*. Timber Press, Cambridge, 2004.

6. Coombes, A. J. *A-Z of Plant Names*. Chancellor Press, London, 1994.

7. *The Plant List*. Version 1.1, 2013. www.theplantlist.org.

8. Wiktorowski, K. *Women and Cacti*. www.kwikirepublika.pl/wom.html.

9. Aitkin, R. *Botanical Riches: Stories of Botanical Exploration*. Lund Humphries, London, 2008.

10. Gibbons, W. *How do you know you have found a new species?* www.srel.uga.edu/ecoview070121.htm

11. Natural History Museum. *Carl Linnaeus*. www.nhm.ac.uk/nature-online/science-online

12. Broberg, G. *Carl Linnaeus*. Swedish Institute, Copenhagen, 2006.

13. Buchan,U. & Colborn, N. *The classic horticulturalist*. Cassell, London, 1987.

14. Morton A.G. *History of Botanical Science*. Academic Press, London, 1981.

15. Pavord, A. *The Naming of Names*. Bloomsbury, London, 2005.

16. Linnaeus, K. *Species Plantarum*. Sweden, 1753.

17. *The Wild Ornamental Plants in the Three Parallel Rivers*

18. McNeill, J. & Turland, N.J. *International Rules of Botanical Nomenclature*. 2011. www.bgbm.fu-berlin.de/iapt/nomenclature/code

19. International Code of Nomenclature for algae, fungi and plants (Melbourne Code). Regnum Vegetabile 154. Koeltz Scientific Books, 2012.

20. International Code of Nomenclature for algae, fungi and plants (Shenzen Code). Regnum Vegitabile 159. Koeltz Scientific Books, 2018.

21. Stearns, W.T. *Dictionary of Plant Names for Gardeners*. Timber Press, Cambridge, 1972

22. Brickell, C.D. *et al. International Code of Nomenclature for Cultivated Plants*. 2016. www.ishs.org/sci/icracpco.htm

23. Lindon, H.L, Hartley, H., Knapp, S., Monro, A.M. & Turland, N.J. *X1X International Botanical Congress, Shenzen: Report of the Nomenclature Section*, 17-21 July 2017. Phytokeys 150, 1-276, 2020.

24. Doring, M. & Stevens, P. *APG1V Angiosperm Phylogeny Group Classification for the Orders and Families of Flowering Plants*. The Catalogue of Life Partnership, 2020.

25. Cheek, M. *The Ugliest Orchid in the World Tops Kew's 2020 New Species*, Royal Botanic Gardens, Kew, 17 December 2020.

CHAPTER TWO
WIVES

Lady Dorothea Banks
Lady Jane Franklin
Lucile Boissier
Eleanor Carmichael Aitchison
Lady Edith Blake
Lady Elizabeth Lawrence
Mary Allen Sargent
Ellen Ganderton Wilson
Florinda Kingdon-Ward
Eva Racine Sarasy Foster
Jean Macklin
Mrs Benson
Martha Erni
Catherine Pancratia Maurandy
Carolina Morren
Juliana Schneider

WIVES

Much of this chapter was written during the Covid-19 lockdowns of 2020-2021 which meant that I had to rely on the Internet as the main source of information since books and journals were less readily available. Moreover, while I was also able to access my own extensive library of botanical books, I discovered very little information about the women in this chapter even though some featured here were botanists or horticulturalists in their own right. This is not surprising since many had plants named after them by virtue of being the wife of a famous botanist or horticulturalist. In fact, the Internet proved to be the best source of information particularly since many early botanical books and journals have been digitised and made available to everyone online, including *The Gardeners' Chronicle* [1], *Curtis's Botanical Magazine* [2] and *Species Plantarum.*[3] A specific mention should be made here of the Biodiversity Heritage Library (www.biodiversitylibrary.org) which is a wonderful resource for researchers.[4]

In reality, it turned out that the sixteen women featured in this chapter are a very diverse bunch! Eleven had husbands well-known within their areas of expertise; not necessarily botanical or horticultural, but for the remaining five women, very little about their lives has been found, and much of that is uncertain or disputed! Beginning with the eleven on which there is definitive information: two were born in the 18th century – Dorothea Banks and Jane Franklin – and had famous husbands. Dorothea was married to Joseph Banks, well-known to all botanists, and Jane to Joseph Franklin the Arctic explorer. Dorothea herself collected china and porcelain and Jane established a botanical garden in Tasmania. Seven of the women were born in the 19th century at the height of botanical exploration and discovery. One of them, Edith Blake, was a botanical artist and should have been included as a plants-woman in her own right in my earlier book, *There She Grows*.[5] Her husband eventually became Governor of The Bahamas. The remaining six women in this group had husbands who were botanists themselves, had interests in botanical collecting outside their main employment or were frequently accompanied on botanical expeditions by their wives. The remaining two women - Racine Foster and Jean Macklin - were born in the 20th century and married well-known botanists, joining their husbands to search for plants. Of these 11 women, five were English, one Scottish and two from Ireland. One lived variously in India or England, two were American and one Swiss. However, while these may have been their countries of birth, some moved around. Thus – Jane Franklin moved from England to Australia, Eleanor Aitchison from Scotland to India, Edith Blake from Ireland to various parts of the British Empire, Ellen Wilson from England to the USA, and Florinda Kingdon-Ward from Ireland to England. In other words, this was a mobile population, reflecting their husbands' occupations and status in life.

This leaves five women about whom I have been unable to find much, if any, definitive information: Mrs Benson, Martha Erni, Catherine Maurandy, Carolina Morren and Juliana Schneider. Although much is known about Mrs Benson's husband, an orchid expert born in 1785, her first name has not been found.

Then there are two disputed wives: Martha Erni is named as the wife of Franz Sales Erni, but in accounts of his life she is named as Katherine Schwenn; and Carolina Morren is the wife of Charles Morren, a Belgian botanist, but elsewhere she is named as Euphemie Xhibitte! The confusion around Catherine Maurandy is that she is variously described as a botany student, a professor and the wife of A.J. Maurandy, a botany professor in Spain in the late 18th century. Finally, Juliana Schneider, was undoubtedly the wife of Camillo Karl Schneider, and must have been divorced from her husband before his second marriage in 1925, but details are vague. These five women have even more diverse origins than the 11 mentioned above: possibly moving from England to India, and living in Switzerland, Spain, Belgium and Austria. All of this mixed information is reported under each name. It would probably have been easier to ignore these last five women! However, the one source I used – A.J. Coombes's *A-Z of Plant Names* – was valuable and I had no wish to deviate from my goal by excluding the difficult ones.

The lives of the 11 women in this chapter about whom there is information, are now described in order of their date of birth, with the remaining five listed alphabetically at the end.

Lady Dorothea Banks (1758-1828)

In 1779, heiress Dorothea Hugessen, younger daughter of William Western Hugessen (1736-64) and Thomasine Honywood (1734-98), married Joseph Banks (1743-1820) in London, England and settled in a large house at 32 Soho Square, this being their London residence. Dorothea's mother was the second daughter of Sir John Honywood, 4th baronet who was also an MP.

Dorothea and Joseph Banks were financially secure, mainly from inheritance and were able to maintain a large country house, Spring Grove, in Isleworth, then outside London.[6] They kept both houses until Joseph's death in 1820. They had no children. Joseph also inherited his father's country estate, Revesby Abbey in Lincolnshire once he reached the age of 21 in 1764, following his father's death in 1761.[7] Joseph brought home hundreds of new species of plants, many of which were planted at Revesby. It is also said he brought kangaroos back to the Estate and the part of the park where he lived is still called Kangaroo Park today.

Much has been written about Sir Joseph Banks, one of the most famous botanists in the UK, and indeed, the world. [8-10] The main features of his life are summarised here. Joseph's interest in botany began early when he lived at his father's estate in Lincolnshire and was able to enjoy the local countryside, but at the age of eight he was sent to board at Harrow School, followed by Eton and then Oxford University from where he did not graduate, but where his interest in botany developed further. After he inherited his estate at Revesby Abbey, he became the local squire and magistrate, sharing his time between Lincolnshire and his homes in London. From his mother's home in Chelsea, he kept up his interest in science by attending the Chelsea Physic Garden and the British Museum. In 1767 he was elected President of the Royal Society, a position he held until his death in 1820. As President, he was involved in the activities of the Board of Longitude and the Greenwich Royal Observatory. He sent botanists to all parts of the world, including New South Wales, often at his own expense. The plants they brought back were added to the Royal Botanic Gardens at Kew, where King George III appointed Joseph advisor, and to his own collections. Between 1768 and 1771, Joseph was appointed botanist for James Cook's first voyage to the South Pacific on the Endeavour. The main intent of the voyage was to observe the transit of Venus. Their mission was to reach Tahiti before June 1769 and construct an astronomical observatory. Cook and his crew would observe Venus gliding across the face of the Sun, thus measuring the size of the solar system, or so was the hope of England's Royal Academy, which sponsored the trip.[11] The size of the solar system was one of the chief puzzles of 18th century science. It was known that six planets orbited the sun (Uranus, Neptune, and Pluto hadn't been discovered at that time), and the relative spacing of the six was also known, but not the absolute distances covered. The problem was that transits of Venus are rare; they come in pairs, 8 years apart, separated by approximately 120 years.[12]

The voyage then progressed to New Zealand and to the east coast of Australia, where Cook mapped the coastline and made landfall at Botany Bay and at Endeavour River (near modern Cooktown) in Queensland, where he spent almost seven weeks ashore while the ship was repaired after foundering on the Great Barrier Reef.

All of these adventures occurred before Joseph and Dorothea married in 1779 but were responsible for making the name of Joseph Banks so well-known especially in botanical circles. On the back of Joseph's fame as a botanist, the Banks's entertained many scientists, students and foreign visitors at their London house. He was created a baronet in 1781 and Knight Commander of the Order of the Bath in 1795. Dorothea became Lady Banks in 1781.

Joseph's sister Sarah Sophia Banks (1744-1810) (known as Sophie), who never married, also lived with the Banks's at their house in Soho Square and the three became almost inseparable.[13] Sophie was a renowned collector of coins and other tokens and was put in charge of the hothouses and conservatories at the Spring Grove house. What is less well known is that Dorothea was – like her husband – an avid collector, but not of plants. Shortly after she married, she transformed the dairy building at their Spring Grove house into an exquisite china cabinet. All that remains of that collection today, however, is a manuscript describing some of Dorothea's best items. She has been described as *'A Little Old-China Mad.'*[14]

Joseph became ill with gout and lost the use of his legs after 1805, but his mind remained active. He died on 19 June 1820 in Spring Grove House and was buried at St Leonard's Church, Heston, near London. Dorothea lived for a further eight years until 1828.

What happened to the three residences of the Banks after the death of Dorothea with no direct heirs? Spring Grove House was eventually sold to the great grandson of the Pears Soap inventor and was subsequently used as a hospital after World War 1. It was then acquired by Middlesex County Council as a centre for education.[6] Revesby Abbey was inherited by a distant branch of the Banks family but has subsequently fallen into disrepair, although attempts are being made to restore it to its former glory.[15] The site of the Soho Square house bears a plaque (now in stone to replace an earlier blue plaque) commemorating Joseph Banks with the inscription:

'SIR JOSEPH BANKS 1743-1820 PRESIDENT OF THE ROYAL SOCIETY ROBERT BROWN 1773-1858 AND DAVID DON 1800-1841 BOTANISTS LIVED IN A HOUSE ON THIS SITE THE LINNEAN SOCIETY MET HERE 1821-1857.'[16]

Rosa banksiae

The plant named after Dorothea, *Rosa banksiae*, originated in China and was introduced to Europe by William Kerr, who had been sent on a plant-hunting expedition by Joseph. It was first described and published in 1811 by the botanist William Townsend Aiton (1766-1849). It was also attributed to Robert Brown (1773-1858), a Scottish botanist, but in 2018 the International Code of Nomenclature (ICN) agreed that W.T. Aiton was the true author.[17] *Rosa banksiae* is an evergreen climbing rose with small double pale yellowish flowers which are scented and tend to appear early in the northern hemisphere.

BOTANICAL NAME
Rosa banksiae

COMMON NAME
Lady Banks's Rose

FAMILY
Rosaceae

NATIVE OF CHINA

Lady Jane Franklin (1791-1875)

Jane Franklin has been described as a woman of extraordinary character and personality who was not content to sit at home with her embroidery, defying the norms expected by society in England at the time.[18] Her early life did not start well with her mother dying when she was just four years old. She was born Jane Griffin. Her mother was Jane Guillemard (1765-1795) who had married John Griffin (1757-1852), a silk weaver, in 1786 but after nine years had died leaving him with four young children, aged 8,7,4 and 2. Jane was the third child. She had an older brother, John, who died in 1804 when she was 13, an older sister Frances and a younger one, Mary. After John's death they were a close family of three girls, living with their father in Bedford Place, London.[19] Jane's father John, who became governor of the Goldsmith's Company, ensured that his daughters were well educated.

In 1828, when Jane was 37, she became the second wife of John Franklin (1786-1875), whose first wife, a friend of Jane's, was Eleanor Anne Porden (1795-1825), a poet, who sadly died of tuberculosis in 1825 leaving her husband with a daughter, Eleanor Isabella (1824-1860), then aged just a year old. Eleanor Isabella, herself, married the Rev. John Philip Gell but died aged 36 years after becoming the mother of seven children. [20] Jane and John did not have any children of their own. Shortly after their marriage, in 1829, John was knighted and Jane became Lady Jane Franklin.

John Franklin was born in Spilsby, Lincolnshire, one of twelve children, and had become an officer in the Royal Navy, but was best known for his polar expeditions. He had sailed with Matthew Flinders to Australia and served at the Battles of Trafalgar and New Orleans but then took part in numerous arctic expeditions exploring the Hudson Bay and the Arctic Ocean, as well as searching for the North-West Passage, all before his marriage to Jane.[21] Two of the voyages searching for the North West Passage were on foot and one was with the ships HMS *Erebus* and HMS *Terror*.[22] In 1837 John was appointed Governor General of Tasmania (then known as Van Diemen's Land) and remained in post until recalled in 1843.[23] During this time Jane, whose particular interest was in education, worked to set up a university, a museum and botanical gardens in Tasmania. In 1839, she became the first European woman to travel overland between Port Philip and Sydney, followed in 1841-42 from Hobart to Macquarie Harbour. With her husband, she encouraged the founding of secondary schools for boys and girls. The Franklins are well thought of in Tasmania to this day with Franklin Square, in the centre of Tasmania's capital, Hobart, being named after them. Furthermore, Jane is commemorated elsewhere: in Lady Franklin Bay, Northern Canada; Lady Franklin Rock in the Fraser River, British Columbia and in Yosemite National Park, California.

Jane's main claim to fame, however, has nothing to do with plants but concerns a tragedy involving her husband, which took place in 1845. What became his last expedition took place after they had returned to England. This expedition set out for the Arctic with two ships, the HMS *Erebus* and HMS *Terror* and 129 crew members but never returned.[18] The fate of the expedition remained a mystery until 2014, long after Jane's death, when the *Erebus* was discovered by a Canadian expedition, followed two years later by the *Terror*.[24]

Although search parties were sent out to try to discover the fate of the expedition it was the tenacity of Jane's tireless efforts to continue to search for the ships which led to this being one of the most well-known mysteries of the age. Although well-travelled herself, Jane did not go to the Arctic but instead sponsored seven expeditions and at one point purchased her own ship in heroic efforts to discover the fate of her husband, causing her to be described as *'The 19th century's most famous widow.'* [25] After the disappearance of her husband, Jane travelled widely, visiting Japan, India and USA and Hawaii frequently with her niece, Sophia Cracroft as her secretary and companion; something unusual for women of her generation. Jane died in 1875 aged 84 years, still not knowing her husband's fate, and is buried in Kensal Green Cemetery, London. She is commemorated on a cross dedicated to her niece, Sophia Cracroft. A biography of Jane's life can be found in Alison Alexander's book. [26]

Jane's botanical interests were inspired when, in 1839, she purchased land near Hobart to set up of a botanical garden which she named Acanthe (Blooming Valley). The collections she had been establishing in Government House were housed in a Museum of Natural History, built for this purpose in the style of a Greek temple. They and the accompanying library were dispersed in 1853, and the miniature temple became a storehouse for apples, the cultivation of which had been one of Jane's interests. Currently Acanthe Park in Hobart still houses the building which, after becoming derelict, is now run by the Arts Society of Tasmania. [27]

The plant selected here and named after Jane is *Acradenia frankliniae* which was discovered in 1842 along the Franklin River in Tasmania by Dr Joseph Milligan, an Australian botanist, and introduced to

Kew in 1845. Jane and her husband were with Dr Milligan when the plant was discovered.[28] *Acradenia frankliniae*, commonly known as whitey wood, is a member of the Rutaceae (Rue) family and was first described in 1852 by Richard Kippist (1812-82), a botanist at the Linnean Society, London.[29] It is an evergreen shrub with aromatic leaves and white flowers, growing up to 3m. in height. The flowers are grouped into multi-flowered heads in late spring.

BOTANICAL NAME
Acradenia frankliniae

COMMON NAME
Wirewood/Whitey Wood

FAMILY
Rutaceae

NATIVE OF TASMANIA

Also named after Jane is the filmy fern *Hymenophyllum frankliniae* discovered by Ernst Dieffenbach, a naturalist, and William Colenso, a botanist, who Jane had met in New Zealand in 1841.[30]

Hymenophyllum frankliniae

39

Lucile Boissier (1822-1849)

The story of Lucile Boissier (née Butini) is a sad one. She died at the age of only 27 years but her name is immortalized in the names of two plants. How did she achieve this at such a young age? The secret is that she was the wife of the Swiss botanist, Pierre Edmond Boissier (1810-1885) who was twelve years her senior.

In 1840 Lucile Butini had married her cousin, Edmond Boissier as he was generally known, and often accompanied him on trips in search of plants in Europe, North Africa and the Middle East. Lucile's father, Adolphe Pierre Butini, born in 1792, was the brother of Edmond's mother, Caroline Louise Butini (1785-1836). Lucile and Edmond shared grandparents, Pierre Butini (1759-1838), a naturalist, and Jeanne Pernette Bardin (1764-1841).[31]

Ompholodes luciliae

Lucile's husband, had inherited a fortune from his family and could have had a life of '*luxurious idleness*'[32] but decided instead to take up botany and went on to become one of the most prolific plant collectors of the 19th century. He was particularly noted for monographs on the family Plumbaginaceae and the genus *Euphorbia*. His most important work was the *Flora Orientalis* published in five volumes between 1867 and 1884).[32-33]

Unfortunately, on one of his plant collecting trips to Spain and Algeria in 1849 Lucile died of an infection. Her husband then named *Ompholodes luciliae*,[34] also known as navelwort, in memory

BOTANICAL NAME
Ompholodes luciliae

COMMON NAME
Navelwort/Rock forget-me-not

FAMILY
Boraginaceae

NATIVE OF TURKEY

Chionodoxa luciliae

of his dead wife because its flower colour was the same blue as her eyes.[31,35] Edmond found it difficult to recover from the loss of Lucile and, as J.M.C wrote in 1886, *'the rest of his life was spent in the shadow of this sorrow...'* [32] In 1877, he named another plant after her: *Chionodoxa luciliae*.[36,37] This plant is also known as Lucile's Glory of the Snow. Both plants named after Lucile are natives of Turkey, with *Chionodoxa luciliae* being a member of the Lily family whilst *Ompholodes luciliae* is of the Boraginaceae family.

BOTANICAL NAME
Chionodoxa luciliae

COMMON NAME
Glory-of-the-snow

FAMILY
Liliaceae

NATIVE OF TURKEY

Lucile and Edmond had two children, a son Agenor Edmond Boissier (1841-1913), and a daughter Caroline Mathilde Boissier (1847-1918), who was only two years old when her mother died.[38] In later years, Caroline Barbey-Boissier (1847-1918) collected plants with her father and went on to marry the Swiss naturalist William Barbey (1842-1914), with whom she developed a large herbarium.

They had seven children. Caroline inherited the agricultural estate of Valleyres-sous-Rances in Switzerland and enlarged the botanical garden set up by her father, Edmond Boissier. William Barbey was also philanthropic in caring for the workers on the estate.[39] After Lucile's husband Edmond Boissier's death in 1885 there was concern that his herbarium should find a suitable home and it was finally located in the Conservatory and Botanic Gardens in Geneva where it is still widely consulted.[40] A picture of Lucile Boissier has not been located.[41]

Eleanor Carmichael Aitchison (1840-1897)

The plant *Rosa ecae* has an unusually derived name. It was brought to the UK in 1880 by Surgeon-Major James Edward Tierney Aitchison (1835-98) who was an army surgeon in the Afghan war of that time, and was named after the initials of his wife's name: Eleanor Carmichael. Little information is known about Eleanor, but rather more about her husband. Much of the information is from his obituary in the Transactions and Proceedings of the Botanical Society of Edinburgh in 1898.[42] Here, Eleanor is described as a '*lady of charming manners.*'

Eleanor Carmichael Craig was the second of the eight children of Robert Craig (1808-1892) and Margaret Reid (born 1810). Robert Craig's mother, and Eleanor's grandmother, was named Eleanor Carmichael,[43] and her grandfather was James Craig (1980-1841).

According to Dr Aitchison's obituary, his eldest sister was married to Rev. Dr Gordon of Newbattle near Dalkeith in Scotland where Aitchison spent Sunday afternoons when he was young. It was here that he met Eleanor, wo lived at Craigesk,

NEWBATTLE OLD BRIDGE

a large house belonging to her father, near Newbattle. They married in 1862 when Eleanor was 22 and her husband 27. The house still stands alongside the River South Esk overlooking what was the papermill (largely demolished in 1894), set up by James Craig and the source of the family's wealth.[44]

After the death of James Craig in 1841, the papermill was taken on by his son Robert, Eleanor's father, as Robert Craig and Sons Ltd.

Much of the land in the area of Newbattle was owned by the Marquis of Lothian. When the lease on the papermill at Lothian Bridge, Newbattle, was up for renewal in 1890, agreement could not be reached to extend it so the work was moved to Robert Craig's other papermills at Caldercruix and Moffat. This meant that about 300 workers, mainly women, lost their jobs and the closure was a serious blow to the local economy.[45]

ELEANOR'S HUSBAND

So, what of Eleanor's husband, James? He was the son of Major J. Aitchison, was born in India, studied medicine and surgery at Edinburgh, and entered the Bengal Medical Service in 1858, remaining in it for thirty years. However, he was very interested in botany, something he had learned from his mother, Mary Turner, and made a great contribution to the botany of India and Afghanistan.[46-49] He was variously described as lively, kindly and genial and loved sports, particularly tennis and cricket. His health suffered,

however, not helped by his many botanical expeditions, on most of which he was accompanied by Eleanor. It has been suggested that these trips were detrimental to Eleanor's health, perhaps contributing to her early death in 1897 at the age of 57 years.

Rosa ecae

Dr Aitchison was badly affected by his wife's death and died a year after her at Kew, London, aged 63, to where they had retired because of his own ill health.[42] He is buried at Newbattle.

The rose, *Rosa ecae*, also known as Mrs. Aitcheson's Rose, was first identified by Eleanor's husband in Afghanistan and described in 1880.[50] The flowers, borne on a compact shrub, are small and buttercup yellow in colour, each only an inch or so across and growing along the dark brown, thorny branches. The leaves are small and fern-like in appearance. The shrub is easy to grow but prefers a warm, sunny position.

BOTANICAL NAME
Rosa ecae

COMMON NAME
Mrs Aitchison's Rose

FAMILY
Rosaceae

NATIVE OF
AFGHANISTAN

Lady Edith Blake (1845-1926)

Bauhinia blakeana, named for Edith Blake
and her husband, appears at the centre
of the new flag of Hong Kong. It
was introduced when the country
gained independence from
Britain in 1997. Here is how it
happened.

Edith was Irish, born into a family
of landed gentry at Newtown,
Tipperary in 1845. Her father,
Ralph Bernal Osborne (1808-1882)
was a liberal MP for various English
constituencies and her mother, Catherine Isabella Osborne (1818-1880) was the
daughter of Sir Thomas Osborne, 9th baronet whose Irish estates
included copper mines.[51] On their marriage in 1844 Ralph took
his wife's surname changing from his birth name of Ralph Bernal
to Ralph Bernal Osborne. The Osborne's lived apart for much of
their marriage with Ralph in England and Catherine at Newtown
Anner Hall in Ireland where she brought up their two daughters. It
is said that Ralph married Catherine for her money.[51] Edith was the
elder daughter and her younger sister, Grace married the 10th Duke
of St. Albans. Apparently, Edith shocked her family in 1874 when,
rather than marrying her mother's choice of husband, she eloped
with Captain Henry Blake (1840-1918), a widower, of the Royal
Irish Constabulary, and was disinherited because of his lower social
status. His mother considered him to be a *'fortune hunter.'* Edith was
undeterred and was rewarded with a long and happy marriage. The
Blakes had three children, Olive (1875 -1953), Maurice and Arthur.

Edith inherited her artistic talents from her mother and eventually became an accomplished botanical artist, but before that she had to face an uncertain beginning to married life with a husband of limited means with a widowed mother and 12 brothers and sisters to support. However, they prospered and eventually Henry became a Special Magistrate in Ireland, but caused some controversy and entered the Colonial Service of the British Empire, becoming Governor of the Bahamas in 1884-87, when Edith was 40 years old.[52] This was the point when life took off for the couple and Edith is reported to have delighted in her life overseas.[53] The Bahamas posting was followed by similar ones over the following 27 years to Newfoundland (1887-9) (where Henry was knighted), Jamaica (1889-1897), Hong Kong (1897-1903) and Ceylon (Sri Lanka) (1903-7)).[53]

During all of these postings, Edith continued to paint and while in Jamaica produced a collection of over 200 watercolours of butterflies and moths as well as plants.[54] Edith's paintings were exhibited in Dublin in 1894 and bequeathed to the British Museum in London by her daughter Olive Arbuthnot. They are now held in the Natural History Museum, also in London. Moreover, she was an accomplished linguist and wrote two books and three plays as well as contributing to magazines such as *The Illustrated London News*.[51] Her writings on the Maroons of Jamaica (Africans who escaped from slavery to established free communities in the mountains of Jamaica) attracted considerable attention.[55] Like many men with similar postings to overseas territories, including the husbands of Racine Foster, Mrs Benson and Eleanor Aitcheson, also featured in this book, Henry was very interested in botany.[5] Together, Edith and Henry were collectors of Jamaican flora[56] and Edith sent plants to Kew.

Bauhinia blakeana was identified and named during Henry's posting to Hong Kong between 1897 and 1903. Henry identified the new species on the seashore of Hong Kong Island and it was named by Stephen Troyte Dunn who was the Superintendent of the Hong Kong Botanical and Forestry Department.[57] The paper identifying this as a new species includes the following words:

'*The trivial name of this species commemorates the kindly interest taken in the Hongkong Botanic Gardens by Sir Henry and Lady Blake during the Governorship of the former, which ended in 1903.*'

This extract firmly places the plant as being named for both Edith and her husband.[58] In addition to *Bauhinia blakeana,* two oak trees from Hong Kong were named for the couple – *Quercus blakei* for Henry and *Quercus edithae* for Edith.[56,59]

Although known as the Hong Kong Orchid, *Bauhinia blakeana* is not an orchid, but a member of the Fabaceae (Leguminoseae) family, probably named as the Hong Kong Orchid because its flowers very much resemble orchids. First identified in 1880 by Delavay, a French catholic missionary and botanist, who took a cutting from which all existing *Bauhinia blakeana* plants are thought to have originated, the plants are sterile hybrids of the pink-flowered butterfly tree (*Bauhinia variegata*), and the purple-flowered *Bauhinia purpurea*. As noted above, the first published description of the

Bauhinia blakeana

BOTANICAL NAME
Bauhinia blakeana

COMMON NAME
Hong Kong Orchid Tree

FAMILY
Fabaceae

NATIVE OF HONG KONG

species was in 1908 by Stephen Troyte Dunn, a British botanist with a particular interest in Chinese plants.[58] Despite not producing seeds, large numbers of the trees can be found around the world, all originating as cuttings, and widely valued for their ornamental char- acteristics.[60] The orchid tree was chosen as Hong Kong's emblem on its flag because it

represents the merging of old and new. It is even depicted on coins of Hong Kong.[61]

Henry retired in 1907 when he and Edith moved to Myrtle Grove, Youghal, County Cork, a large house still occupied by members of the family today. Many of Edith's sketchbooks are still at the house and she decorated the staircase with botanical illustrations. Henry died in 1918 and Edith remained at the house rarely leaving until her death 8 years later in 1926. Edith and Henry are both buried in the garden of Myrtle Grove.[52]

In retrospect, Lady Edith Blake should have merited a place in my earlier book *There She Grows* which covered 35 women who were plants-women in their own right, as artists, botanists, horticultur- alists or collectors.[5]

Lady Elizabeth Lawrence (1845-1916)

Lady Elizabeth Lawrence was born Elizabeth Matthew. She was the daughter of John Matthew, an industrialist (1819-1869) and Maria Hartree (1819-1874) and married into the aristocracy. John Matthew, the son of a Russian merchant, was a very successful marine engineer who made his fortune as a director of the company John Penn & Son of Greenwich, England which specialised in marine steam engines.[62]

There was much intermarriage within the company. Charlotte, sister to John Penn, the head of the company, married William Hartree in 1839. It is likely that William was already an apprentice with the firm of which he became a partner in 1848. William Hartree's sister Maria married John Matthew who became an apprentice with the firm in 1840 and during that decade, chief designer and the third partner of the firm. William Hartree was the great grandfather of mathematician and physicist Douglas Hartree (1897-1958). These inter-relationships mean that Elizabeth's mother, Maria, was sister to one of the firm's directors and her father, John, was also a director.[63]

John Matthew owned a house near Box Hill which was inherited by Eliz-

Aerides lawrenceae

BOTANICAL NAME
Aerides lawrenceae

COMMON NAME
Lady Lawrence's aerides

FAMILY
Orchidaceae

NATIVE OF PHILIPPINES

abeth, an only living child; a younger brother, Matthew, having died young. The house was known as Burford Lodge, near Dorking.[64] It was later sold and the site and buildings have been converted to flats, houses and a hotel. John Matthew died in 1869 at the age of 50, when Elizabeth was just 24 years old and in the year of her marriage to Sir Trevor Lawrence (1831-1913). Sir Trevor and Lady Lawrence took up residence at Burford Lodge and continued to live there for the rest of their lives. It was her marriage to Sir Trevor, fourteen years her senior, which propelled her into the world of horticulture. He was the son of the renowned horticulturalist and orchid afficionado Louisa Lawrence, from whom he inherited his love of orchids.[5] The orchid *Brassia lawrenciana* (Lawrence's Brassia) was named for Louisa. Louisa Lawrence features in the companion volume to this one: *There She Grows*.[5] Sir Trevor's interest in orchids was further developed during his time in the Indian Medical Service. He was the son of the first baronet Sir William Lawrence, a surgeon to Queen Victoria, and became a surgeon himself. Sir William died shortly after the baronetcy was created and the title was taken by Sir Trevor in 1867 who then pursued a parliamentary career; he was conservative MP for Mid-Surrey, and subsequently became Treasurer of St. Bartholomew's Hospital, his *alma mater*. A knighthood was conferred in 1902. His main interest, however, continued to be in horticulture, particularly orchids and he was President of the Royal Horticultural Society from 1885 to 1913. He was a recipient of the Victoria Medal in 1900 and the Veitch Memorial Gold Medal in 1913, with the Lawrence Gold Medal being founded in his honour.[65] With such an illustrious career in horticulture it is unsurprising that he ensured that his wife, Elizabeth, had a plant named after her.

Sir Trevor died in 1913 and by that time was one of the world's leading orchid collectors. He had asked Elizabeth to donate plants of botanical interest to Kew and 580 were thought to qualify. Two specific orchids, *Paphiopedilum lawrenceanum* and *Cattleya lawrenceana* were named after him but, importantly, *Aerides lawrenceae* was named after Elizabeth, so perpetuating her name.[66] The plant was first described in 1883, by Heinrich Gustav Reichenbach, a German botanist and orchidologist.[67] This account in the *Gardeners' Chronicle* notes that the plant was first imported into England by Mr F. Sander and generated considerable excitement. It was then sold to Sir Trevor for the record sum of £235 guineas.[68] *Aerides lawrenceae* is native to The Philippines where it is found at elevations up to 500 meters, preferring sunny locations. Its flowers are large and grow along elongated stems, flowering in late summer. They are heavily scented and long-lasting.[69]

Mary Allen Sargent (1853-1919)

Mary Allen Sargent was the wife of Charles Sprague Sargent (1841 - 1927), an important American botanist and first director of the Arnold Arboretum of Harvard University. Like many wives in this book, little information is available about Mary's life, though her family and ancestors are well-documented and form the basis of this biography. She was born

ARNOLD ARBORETUM

Mary Allen Robeson in Newport, Rhode Island, into an affluent, well-connected American family. She was the only child of Mary Arnold Robeson (née Allen) (1819-1903) and Andrew Robeson Jr. (1817-1874). Her paternal grandparents were Andrew Robeson Sr, (1787-1862) and Anna Robeson (1787-1848) and her maternal grandparents Zachariah Allen Jr. (1795-1882) and Eliza Harriet Allen (1796-1873).

The Robeson family tree can be traced back many generations to one of many men named Andrew Robeson, the first of whom (1653-1719), moved from Kelso in Scotland to New Jersey in 1676.[70] The Fall River Historical Society records some details of the life of Mary's father, Andrew Robeson Jr. and her grandfather, Andrew Robeson Sr.[71]

In 1821 Andrew Robeson Sr. built an imposing mansion on South Second Street, New Bedford, Massachusetts, with beautiful gardens. Robeson was a leading merchant in the area, with interests in whaling, banking, and printing. In 1978, the mansion, still standing, was relocated to the New Bedford Whaling National History Museum.[72] In 1842, Andrew Robeson Sr, a prominent New Bedford businessman, gave a two-acre plot at 28 Columbia

Street, Fall River, to his son, Andrew Robeson, Jr. (Mary's father), and his daughter-in-law, Mary Arnold Allen (Mary's mother), as a wedding gift. The following year, a large mansion of native granite was constructed on the site. The elegant residence included a wine cellar, which Andrew Robeson Jr., an abolitionist, is said to have converted for use as a secret room to hide runaway slaves.[71] Entrance to the hidden room was accessed via a doorway concealed behind a false panel of books in the library which is still evident in the house today.

Mary's father had graduated in medicine from Pennsylvania State University in Philadelphia but instead of becoming a doctor, joined the company Andrew Robeson & Sons in 1840, and after 1848 took control of the Fall River Print Works (textile printing) until his death in 1874. He was also engaged in business in Boston after 1862, and spent his winters there. He lived in the Fall River house for just two years (1843-4) then in Newport, Rhode Island from 1849 to 1868, and afterwards at Tiverton near Fall River. He was State representative for Newport from 1861 to 1862. Mary was born in Newport and moved with her family to nearby Tiverton when she was 15 years old. The city of Fall River, in Massachusetts was central to the cotton textile industry and during the 19th century was the largest such centre in the USA, with over one hundred mills in operation by 1920.

Mary's maternal grandfather, Zachariah Allen, was a textile manufacturer, inventor, industrialist, lawyer and civic leader. He was born into an influential family in Providence, Rhode Island, the son of Zachariah Allen Sr. and Ann Crawford. He studied medicine at Brown University but chose to become a lawyer. However, soon after his marriage to Eliza Harriet Arnold he gave up the law and purchased some woollen mills.

It was during this period that he began his career as an inventor, and in 1820, he became the first person to install a hot air furnace in his home. He patented an automatic steam engine cut-off valve in 1833 and fire-proofed his mills, being instrumental in setting up an insurance company with other mill owners. As a member of the Providence town council, he implemented the construction of the city water-works and introduced the first fire engine in the city. He was a member of the Board of Trustees of Brown University, and helped found Rhode Island Historical Society.[73,74] The couple had three daughters, the second of whom was Mary's mother, Mary Arnold Allen.

The only photograph of Mary Allen Sargent is a rather blurry one of her with her family taken around 1884. However, she is described as being *'a charming Boston socialite.'* In 1873 she married Charles Sprague Sargent and had five children. The wedding took place at the

CHARLES & MARY ROBESON SARGENT, MARY /MOLLY, CHARLES & ROBESON, ALICE & HENRIETTA (MRS. GUY LOWELL)

Emmanuel Church in Boston where the family had close associations and with which Mary eventually became a benefactor.[75] They lived at his family's estate, known as Holm Lea, in Brookline,

ARNOLD ARBORETUM

where Charles had grown up and subsequently took over its management as a naturalistic, informal garden. It was conveniently close to the Arnold Arboretum of Harvard University in

Boston, where he was director from 1872 until his death in 1927.[76] Charles was the second son of Henrietta Gray and Ignatius Sargent, a Boston merchant and banker who grew wealthy on railroad investments. After Harvard, Charles joined the Union Army during the American Civil War and later travelled in Europe for three years. He is described as having a rather chilly disposition, engrossed in his horticulture with little interest in what was happening in the wider world. He was Professor of Arboriculture at Harvard and it was noted by the Massachusetts State Governor soon after his death in 1927 that: '*Professor Sargent knew more about trees than any other living person. It would be hard to find anyone who did more to protect trees from the vandalism of those who do not appreciate the contribution that they make to the beauty and wealth of our nation.*'[77]

Mary and Charles' children had illustrious lives of their own, though with some tragedy intermixed. Their eldest child, Henrietta Sargent (1875-1953) was born in Tiverton, Rhode Isand and died in Brookline. She married Guy Lowell, a landscape architect and member of the well-known Boston Lowell family whose most famous buildings are the Museum of Fine Arts in Boston and the New York County Court House. Their eldest son, Andrew 'Bobo' Sargent (1876-1918) was born in Brookline and was married to Maria Cecelia de Acosta. Sadly, he died in his sleep at the early age of 42 years. He was another Harvard graduate, who followed in his father Charles's footsteps and worked as a landscape architect with his brother-in-law Guy Lowell. His mother Mary and sisters Henrietta, Mary, and Alice Sargent gave hymn boards and carved doors in his memory to the Emmanuel Church in Boston where his funeral service was held.[75] Another early death in the family was that of Nathanial Bowditch Potter MD who married Mary Sargent

(1878-1962). He died in 1919 aged 49 in San Francisco from the effects of diabetes for which there was no treatment at that time. Ironically, Potter had devoted his medical career attempting to find a cure for diabetes before succumbing to it himself, shortly after his youngest daughter Mary had died of leukaemia. In 1916 he set up the Memorial Laboratory and Clinic for the Study of Nephritis, Gout and Diabetes in New York in memory of his daughter. In addition, the Potter Metabolic Clinic was set up in Santa Barbara where Potter had gone in an attempt to improve his failing health.[78,79] Mary and Charles's fourth child was Charles Sprague Sargent Jr (1880-1959) who married Dagmore Wetmore. He was a Harvard graduate and a stockbroker with interests in a number of companies. Their youngest child was Alice Robeson Sargent (1882-1946) who was unmarried but was active in Red Cross work and in the Free Hospital in Boston. Her funeral service was also held at the Emmanuel Church.[79]

Mary died at the age of 66, some 8 years before her husband, the funeral service again taking place at the Emmanuel Church in Boston, which had played such a large part in her life. She is buried together with her husband at the Walnut Hills Cemetery in Brookline, Mass.[6] The plant named after Mary is *Lilium sargentiae*,

a native of China.[80] It was found and named by Ernest Wilson, the famous plant collector who lived in a house in the grounds of the Arnold Arboretum and was appointed Assistant Director in 1919.[81] Although the plant was discovered in 1903 while Wilson was in China collecting for James

Lilium sargentiae

Veitch and Sons, it was not until 1912 that it was officially described and named by him, *'in compliment to Mrs Sargent, wife of the distinguished dendrologist, Professor Charles Sprague Sargent, by its discoverer and introducer, as a token of esteem.'*[81] After the death of Mary's husband in 1927

BOTANICAL NAME
Lilium sargentiae

COMMON NAME
Sargent Lily

FAMILY
Liliaceae

NATIVE OF CHINA

Wilson became Keeper of the Arnold Arboretum until his untimely death in 1930.[82] Mary would have known the Wilson family well so it is no surprise that he named a plant after her. Furthermore, and slightly beyond the remit of this book, Mary's son Charles introduced the cultivar *Camellia japonica* 'Mary Allen Sargent.' This is a cherry red flowered seedling of 'Edna Campbell' that resembles the cultivar 'Professor Charles Sargent' in form.

Ellen Ganderton Wilson (1872-1930)

Ellen Ganderton was the wife of the famous plant hunter Ernest Henry 'Chinese' (E.H.) Wilson (1876-1930) an explorer who collected in China, initially for the Veitch Nursery in England and later for the Arnold Arboretum in Boston, USA.[83-87] Ernest's first visit to China was in 1899, and the beginning of his successful career introducing Asiatic plants to the West. In 1902 he returned to England and on June 8, 1902 at St. Georges Church, Edgbaston, married Helen (Ellen) Ganderton, also known as Nellie, the daughter of a gardener from Edgbaston, Birmingham, Warwickshire. Initially they lived at 77 Gloucester Road, Kew, close to Ernest's work at Kew Gardens and where their only child, Muriel Primrose, was born in in 1906. However, Ernest undertook more long expeditions after his marriage, as described below, and Ellen lived for some time with her in-laws, who had not approved of the marriage. Ellen's views about these absences have not survived but it could not have been an easy time for her. However, in later years both Ellen and Muriel accompanied Ernest on several expeditions despite Ellen's lifelong ill-health, of indeterminate cause. He named the two plants *Berberis wilsoniae* and *Rosa helenae*, highlighted here, after her. Ernest wrote of *Rhododendron wilsonae*, another of his named plants that it is *'one of the most beautiful and distinctive of Chinese Rhododendrons'* and *'named in compliment to my wife;'* and that *Rosa murielae* is *'named for my daughter Muriel.'*[88] The picture shows Ellen and Ernest with

Muriel as a child. Muriel Primrose (1906-1976) would eventually marry the American botanist, Dr George Lewis Slate (1899-1976), of the Agricultural Experiment Station in Geneva, New York.

Ernest himself was born at Chipping Campden, Gloucestershire, England, the eldest of the seven children of Anne and Henry Wilson, who ran a floristry business.[89] On leaving school, Ernest was apprenticed at a plant nursery, followed by work as a gardener at Birmingham Botanical Gardens, then at Kew. He also trained to become a teacher of botany at the Royal College of Science in South Kensington. A visit to Boston on his way to China changed his and his family's life when he met Charles Sprague Sargent (1841-1927), the first president of the Arnold Arboretum of Harvard University who became a lifelong collaborator. Ernest's first expedition for the Arnold Arboretum took place from 1906-1909 when he wrote that his wife and family would have to be provided for while he was away.[90] It was around this time that the well-known horticulturalist, Ellen Willmott[5] commented to Sargent that *'it is very sad that such a promising man should be hampered by such an ignorant and short-sighted wife at such an early stage in his career!'*[89] Not the most promising start for Ellen! In fact, Ernest had left England and his family when Muriel was 6 months old and had not returned until her 3rd birthday in May 1909. Late that year, in September the Wilson family finally moved to Boston, and in March 1910 Ernest returned to China. During this latter trip, Ellen and Muriel came back to Birmingham and stayed with Ernest's family yet again. Ernest returned to his family in 1911 but needed medical treatment for injuries incurred while travelling near Chengdu in China. A rock fall had caused a severe injury to Ernest's leg such that there was fear it might have to be amputated, but this was eventually avoided. Ernest was adamant that Ellen should not know or worry about the injury and wanted to tell her himself on his return to England, which took several months.[89,90] Initially the family lived in a small apartment near the Arnold Arboretum in Jamaica Plain, Boston, but appear to have had difficulty settling in to the American way of life. It is said that Ernest could not make up his mind about the USA and never took US citizenship despite living there for over 20 years.[89] Ellen liked neither America nor Americans, though her views might have changed over time.[88-91] Eventually the family moved to a house in the grounds of the Arnold Arboretum and stayed there for the rest of their lives. They also visited Japan, Taiwan and Korea. Ernest commented that *'having them with me makes it much pleasanter and infinitely less lonely for me.'* [89,92] In 1919 Ernest was appointed Assistant Director of the Arnold Arboretum.[88] His last expedition, a tour of the gardens of the world, took place from 1920 to 1922 and included a stop at the Singapore Botanical Garden in June of 1921. In 1927, Ernest became Keeper of the Arnold Arboretum, after the death of Charles Sargent. The former title 'Director' was abandoned at that time and not re-instead until after the tragic death of Ernest in 1930.

Thus, his remarkable career was cut short when he and Ellen were killed in a car crash near Worcester, Massachusetts while returning from a visit to their daughter, Muriel, in northern New York state. It appears that the car spun off the road and plunged down a steep embankment. When help arrived Ellen was already dead and Ernest died a few hours later. Their pet dog escaped with cuts and bruises. The accident might possibly be attributed to Ernest's weak leg after his injury in China in 1911. The funeral took place in Boston, and was attended by shocked horticulturalists from across the USA and beyond, followed by cremation at the Forest Hills cemetery, Jamaica Plain, near the Arnold Arboretum. Muriel wanted her parents to be buried on British soil, and selected Mont-Royal Cemetery in Montreal, Canada where there is a memorial at Lilac Knoll, an area which Ernest helped to design.[89] In recognition of his service to horticulture E.H. Wilson received many awards throughout his life, including the Victoria Medal of Honour of the RHS in 1912, the Veitch Memorial Medal and the George Robert White Memorial Medal of the Massachusetts Horticultural Society.

*Berberis wilsoni*ae was named in 1906 by the English botanist William Hemsley (1843-1924) in honour of Ellen Wilson.[93] It is an evergreen, hermaphrodite shrub which flowers in June and July and can grow in poor quality, dry or moist soils in shady or open areas.

Berberis wilsoniae

Rosa helenae

Rosa helenae was first described in Plantae Wilsonianae by its co-authors, Alfred Rehder and Ernest Wilson while both were working at the Arnold Arboretum.[94] It prefers fertile, humus-rich, moist but well-drained soil in a sheltered, sunny site, in marked contrast to *Berberis wilsoniae*. Both species are native of China.

BOTANICAL NAME
Rosa helenae

COMMON NAME
Helen's Rose

FAMILY
Rosaceae

NATIVE OF CHINA

BOTANICAL NAME
Berberis wilsoniae

COMMON NAME
Wilson Barberry

FAMILY
Berberidaceae

NATIVE OF CHINA

Florinda Kingdon-Ward (1896-1972)

Frank Kingdon-Ward (1885-1958) was a professional plant hunter in Asia:- primarily China, Tibet and Burma. His particular fame was in bringing the blue poppy, *Meconopsis*, to Britain.[95] He had two wives, Florinda and Jean, and named plants after both of them: *Primula florindae* considered here, and *Lilium mackliniae* elsewhere in this book. Florinda Norman-Thompson became Frank's first wife in 1923 at a time when his health was poor and he had little money. She was the youngest of the six children of Robert Norman-Thompson (1853-1907) who died when she was young.[96] He owned a Dublin estate and her mother, Helen Constance Orpin (1858-1915) also owned land near Belfast. After their marriage Florinda and Frank moved to Hatton Gore, a house near London, (now consumed by Heathrow Airport) where he built a rockery which was designed to appear like a bend in a river gorge in the Himalayas. However, he had to sell the house due to a loss he made running a plant nursery business. By 1934 Florinda, and their two daughters, Pleione and Martha, lived at Cleeve Court in Streatley-on-Thames, England. The goddess Pleione features in Chapter 4 of this book.

Frank's father was Harry Marshall Ward (1854-1906) who became Professor of Botany at Cambridge University and his mother was Selina Mary Ward (neé Kingdon) (1864-1922), the daughter of an Exeter lace maker. Frank attended Christ's College, Cambridge but had to leave on his father's early death in 1906.[85] Frank's expeditions to Asia began in 1909 and continued for over forty years. During this time he collected over 100 different plant species, not all of which were new to science, and which included *Rhododendron wardii, Meconopsis betonicifolia, Gaultheria wardii, Acer sikkimense, Lilium wardii, and Lilium mackliniae.* as well as *Primula florindae.*[97]

Despite not being especially interested in exploration or botany, Florinda and her gardeners maintained the garden of Cleeve Court for the plants Frank brought back from his expeditions. Florinda felt it was her duty to support her husband because this was expected of a wife at that time. She introduced him to people who might help to promote his travels, lectures and writing. However, the marriage soon began to fail as Frank spent more time abroad than at home and even missed the births of both his daughters, going on about twenty-five expeditions over a period of nearly fifty years.[98]

In 1937 Florinda and Frank divorced at a time when this was comparatively rare. Then in 1947, Florinda herself stood unsuccessfully for Parliament as the Liberal candidate for Lewes, having rejected the privileged lifestyle inherited after her father's death. She was also a business woman and ran a taxi firm before they were common, and a company producing herbal medicines. She never remarried.[95] *Primula florindae* was first described in the Notes of the Royal Botanic Garden, Edinburgh in 1926.[99] It is an herbaceous perennial with yellow flowers on long stems, and is widely grown.

BOTANICAL NAME
Primula florindae

COMMON NAME
Giant Himalayan Cowslip
or Tibetan Cowslip

FAMILY
Primulaceae

NATIVE OF TIBET

After his divorce, Frank married Jean Macklin and they remained together until his death in 1958. She also features in this book.

Eva Racine Sarasy Foster (1910-1991)

Racine Foster was born In Wisconsin and
attended the High School in Janesville.
Her father, Ralph J Sarasy (1871-1951)
was born in Chicago and was a phar-
macist who managed various drug
stores in Janesville. He was the
son of Jacob and Carrie Hodgdon
Sarasy. He married Racine's mother,
Florence Jessie Craigo (1889-1977) in
Indiana in 1907 and they had 3 daughters,
Racine being the eldest, and one son.[100]

Racine was the second wife of Mulford Bateman Foster (1888–
1978), 22 years her senior, who was known as the 'Father of the
Bromeliad' as he was responsible for the discovery and introduction of many new species of Bromeliad to the United States. They
married in 1935 and had no children. Mulford's first wife, whom
he married in 1911, was Fridel Tautenhahn (1888-1974). They had
four children but divorced in 1933.[100] However, this meant that
Mulford did have a large family of children and grandchildren for
company in his later years. The Fosters were based in Florida and in
1953 had purchased a house known as Bromel-La on a 12-acre plot
near Orlando. Here, bromeliads and other plants collected on their
expeditions were tended, hybridised and developed for over 20 years.

Racine and Mulford had met through Louise Bovington who had
engaged Mulford to landscape her extensive garden at the same time
as Racine tutored her children. Racine and Mulford met and fell
in love while he was still married to his first wife, but divorce was

imminent.[101] They married after Mulford's first visit to Mexico in an informal ceremony at which Racine played the organ as a prelude to the service which took place outside. The honeymoon was spent collecting water plants for Louise's new pond. From then onwards Racine accompanied her husband on his many plant-hunting expeditions[101] and became a notable horticulturalist herself.[102]

Mulford was an expert on bromeliads which he first encountered in 1934 on an expedition to Mexico and was responsible for discovering over 175 new species.[102] He was also a naturalist, explorer, writer, photographer, artist, horticulturist and well-respected landscape architect in Florida.[102] He covered thousands of miles in search of new species. Described as quiet and unassuming, Racine herself was primarily a musician and writer but after her marriage, committed her life to the promotion and enhancement of her husband's career as a horticulturalist and botanist.[102] She was his devoted companion and was happy to further his botanical career at the expense of her own. She worked hard to help him prepare manuscripts, develop theories, prepare specimens and inspire him to move on to greater things. Together, Racine and Mulford explored many parts

A
Lecture
SURPRISE
that is
Startling
Delightful
and
Unexpected

"My Forest Folk in Virgin Valley"
A Romance of The Great-Out-of-Doors by
MULFORD B. FOSTER, Blue Ridge Naturist
Master of One of the Wildest Valleys in Pennsylvania

BROCHURE ADVERTISING THE LECTURES
GIVEN BY MULFORD FOSTER

of the world in their quest for new plant species, and wrote detailed and interesting letters about their adventures.[103] In Columbia they endured hot and humid as well as freezing conditions and in 1946 came across a magnificent area of palms about which Racine wrote in one of her letters *'that is what happens to 'palm nuts' looking for palm nuts?'* In fact, as Herb Piever noted, Racine was a legend in her own right.[104] She catalogued and photographed flora, fauna and terrain and developed a herbarium of plant specimens. These latter were sent to Dr Lyman B. Smith for identification, as in the case of *Aechmea racinae* profiled here. It was also Racine's responsibility to grow on and maintain the collection, especially during the many times that Mulford was away.[104]

Sadly, in 1974 Mulford suffered a stroke which left him paralysed and dependent on a wheelchair but still able to sketch, eventually dying at home on 1978 at the age of 90.[102] At this time Racine was 68 and lived for another 13 years. Diane Racine, a great-granddaughter of Mulford and his first wife, has written a detailed biography of her great-grandfather which includes some further insights into his personality. She quotes Racine saying, after the death of her husband: *'It has been a year since the worst day of my life occurred, this*

DOWNTOWN BUSINESS DISTRICT. ORLANDO, PRESENT DAY. MULFORD AND RACINE FOSTER HAD A RESIDENCE HERE.

date 1978. I must say that I have been trying to learn the meaning of Mulford's departure. Essentially, it is to love more, in a different way, his gentle presence.'[101] It had been hoped that their house could be retained as a bromeliad sanctuary and showcase but this did not happen and Bromel-La had to be sold. However, a memorial fund was established at the Marie Selby Botanical Gardens in Sarasota, Florida where the Mulford B Foster Identification Centre was set up to promote interest in the study of Bromeliads. After the death of her husband Racine continued to work as an experienced horticulturalist until her death in Florida in 1991 at the age of 81 years.

Aechmea racinae, known as Christmas Jewels because it tends to bloom at Christmas, belongs to the family Bromeliaceae and originates from Eastern Brazil.[105,106] Mulford discovered it in 1941 on one of his collecting trips in Brazil, and named it after Racine.[107,108] It is an epiphytic evergreen perennial with red and yellow flowers in the form of a raceme. It has the Royal Horticultural Society's Award of Garden Merit, and is frequently grown as a house plant.[107] The Bromeliaceae is a very large family consisting of 58 genera and over 3400 species found at altitudes of over 3000m, from the southern USA, and in South America from Argentina to Chile. There is just one species, *Pitcairnia feliciana* in Africa. The family is named after Olaus Bromelius (1639-1707) who was a Swedish doctor and botanist.[109] The genus Racinaea, with 80 species, was also named after Racine.

Racinaea tetrantha

BOTANICAL NAME
Aechmea racineae

COMMON NAME
Christmas Jewels

FAMILY
Bromeliaceae

NATIVE OF BRAZIL

Jean Macklin (Mrs Kingdon-Ward) (1921-2011)

Jean Macklin's life can be conveniently divided into three parts: her early life as Jean Macklin (1921-47); her years married to Francis (Frank) Kingdon-Ward (1888-1958) as Jean Kingdon-Ward (1947- 1958) and her later years married to Albert Henry Rasmussen (1883- 1972) as Jean Rasmussen (1958 - 1972).[110]

Jean was the daughter of a Bombay high court judge, Sir Albert Sortain Romer Macklin (1886-1946), and was born there in 1921. She grew up in both India and England.[110]

In 1947, when she was 26 years old, she met and married Francis (Frank) Kingdon-Ward (1888-1958) who was 62 at the time. His first wife was Florinda whom he had married in 1923 and divorced in 1937 (see details in this volume). Jean's parents were opposed to her marrying Frank because of the age difference, but it went ahead despite this and Jean accompanied her husband who was a well-known botanist and plant hunter, on many of his expeditions. She remained married to him until his death, aged 72 in 1958, when she was still only 37 years old. Frank had discovered *Lilium mackliniae* in 1946, prior to his marriage to Jean, but returned with her to India in 1948 and named the plant after her. The details were published by Joseph Robert Sealy (1907-2000), a botanist working at Kew, in 1949.[111] The plant was found on Mount Siroi in Manipur at 1730–2590m., where it still grows in abundance today.[112] Its common name is Siroi Lily. Jean and Frank called their base at Ukhrul, Manipur state, 'Cobweb Cottage alias Bug Bungalow'.

Jean enjoyed going on plant hunting trips with her husband and endured many disasters including being caught in an earthquake of magnitude 8.7 in India in 1950. During this time she became an accomplished botanist in her own right.[110] Frank suffered from numerous illnesses including malaria and vertigo as well as surviving innumerable accidents, which included being impaled on a spike of bamboo and falling off a cliff.[83] His end finally came after ten years of marriage to Jean when he died from a severe stroke.[98] Jean wrote about her adventurous life with Frank in her book, *My Hill So Strong*, published in 1952.[113] As well as *Lilium mackliniae*, Frank is particularly known for collecting *Meconopsis betonicifolia*, the Himalayan Blue Poppy and *Primula florindae*, the Giant Cowslip (named after his first wife) and as the author of a large number of books.[98] At the time of its introduction *Lilium mackliniae* received the Merit Prize in 1948 at the Royal Horticultural Society Flower Show in London (but no longer holds an Award of Garden Merit). It was also commemorated by the Indian Postal Department with a postage stamp and is the State Flower of Manipur.

Shortly after Frank's death, Jean married Albert Henry Rasmussen (known as Ras), a Norwegian, and spent the final phase of her life in Norway.[110] Jean had met Ras many years before they married and had visited him in Norway on several occasions. Like Frank, Ras was many years Jean's senior. At the time of their marriage, she was 37 and he was 75 years old. The two men were similar in many ways, both having been adventurers. Ras had spent over 30 years in China and may have encountered Jean and/or Frank there. Eventually he returned to Norway and became a writer. Jean set about creating a botanical garden around their house, growing Rhododendrons in particular. Unfortunately, her garden was too cold and wet for *Lilium mackliniae* to grow! She also took up photography

Lilium mackliniae

and had an interest in space exploration. After Ras's death at the age of 89, when Jean was still only 51 years old, she moved to Oslo. In later life she retired to Eastbourne in England and died there in 2011 at the age of 90 years,[114] having spent the final 40 or so years of her life alone. Her life had been long and adventurous.[110] The Siroi Lily is an attractive member of the Liliaceae family with pinkish-white bell-shaped flowers, several per stem, which can reach up to 45 cm tall. The bulbs flower in spring and prefer moist, acidic soil and partial shade. Although localised in the wild they can readily be cultivated in gardens.[115]

BOTANICAL NAME
Lilium mackliniae

COMMON NAME
Siroi Lily

FAMILY
Liliaceae

NATIVE OF INDIA

Mrs Benson

Mrs. Benson was the wife of the English General Richard Benson (1785-1858) who collected orchids when he was based in Burma in the 1800s. He was appointed Military Secretary to the Governor General of India, William Bentinck, from 1828 to 1833 and Resident to Ava, the capital city in what became known as Burma and now Myanmar, from 1838 to 1839.[116] It is likely that Mrs Benson lived in India with her husband, travelling to Shimla in the hot summer

Dendrobium bensoniae

months, though no information about her has been found. However, in *Curtis's Botanical Magazine* it is noted that the '*indefatigable collector and horticulturalist*' Colonel Benson had sent a sample of what became *Dendrobium bensoniae*, to Messrs. Veitch '*after whose lady it is named after his own request.*'[117] *Dendrobium bensoniae* was first described by Heinrich Gustav Reichenbach, a German botanist, in 1867.[118] Similarly, Joseph Hooker wrote almost identically in a later edition of *Curtis's Botanical Magazine* how *Thunia bensoniae* (Mrs Benson's Thunia) was described from a specimen sent to the UK from Burma by '*an indefatigable collector and horticulturist, Colonel Benson, after whose lady it is named at his own request.*'[119]

BOTANICAL NAME
Dendrobium bensoniae

COMMON NAME
Lady Benson's Dendrobium

FAMILY
Orchidaceae

NATIVE OF MYANMAR AND THAILAND

Despite these events, Mrs Benson's first name or dates have not been found.

Thunia species are generally terrestrial in habit but sometimes grow semi-epiphytically, often rooted in moss on the surface of trees, but without causing any harm. Flower tend to be large and handsome but short-lived.[120] *Thunia bensoniae* is rare in the wild with showy pink flowers hanging down from stems or 'canes' which tend to project at right angles from their support. For this reason, they are also known as Cane Orchids, and have a slight acrid odour.[121] *Dendrobium bensoniae* orchids require high humidity and should be watered once a day. They are epiphytes with medium-sized white and yellow flowers which hang down in a similar way to those of *Thunia bensoniae*.[122]

Thunia bensoniae

BOTANICAL NAME
Thunia bensoniae

COMMON NAME
Mrs Benson's Thunia

FAMILY
Orchidaceae

NATIVE OF MYANMAR
AND THAILAND

The Missing Wives

It is not surprising that accurate information, or indeed any information, has proved difficult to find for some of the women featured in this book. Some had well known husbands but many biographies fail to provide much information about their wives, other than their names, and these are sometimes incorrect, as indicated below.

There are four women; Martha Erni, Catherine Pancratia Maurandy, Carolina Morren and Juliana Schneider to whom this applies:

Martha Erni

In Coombes' *A to Z of Plant Names*, the reference book used to identify women for this book[80] *Lithops marthae* (Living Stones) is said to have been named after the discoverer's wife, Martha Erni. Other sources state that it was collected

Lithops marthae

by Franz Sales Erni (1878-1952) in 1931, and named for his wife, Martha[80,123-125] No doubt these sources simply copied each other. The problem arises when searching for Martha Erni in biographies of Franz Sales Erni, a well-known Swiss plant collector and botanist who spent much of his life in Southern Africa.[126] In fact, these sources state categorically that he married Katharina Helene Charlotte Wilhelmine Schwenn in 1905, leaving Martha's real identity something of a puzzle.

Lithops marthae[127], also known as *Lithops schwantesii* var. *marthae*[128] or *Lithops schwantesii*[129] is a member of the Aizoaceae family, which contains around 135 genera, including *Mesembryanthemums*.

Lithops marthae is a tiny succulent that grows almost completely buried in the soil with only the upper truncated portion of leaves visible. It has two thick, fleshy leaves from which a yellow flower appears. Old leaves persist for one or two years. The fruit is 5-6 chambered, boat-shaped, with the top more or less flat and the faces elliptical in appearance.

BOTANICAL NAME
Lithops marthae

COMMON NAME
Living Stones

FAMILY
Aizoaceae

NATIVE OF SOUTH AFRICA

Catherine Pancratia Maurandy

The genus *Maurandya* is named in honour of the wife of A J Maurandy, a botany professor at Carthagena University, Spain in the late 18th century. The species *Maurandya scandens* was first described in 1793 by Antonio José Cavanilles (1745-1804), a Spanish taxonomist. He named it *Usteria scandens*,

Maurandya scandens

but discovered the genus name was already in use. it was Casimiro Gómez Ortega (1741-1818) a physician and botanist of the Royal Botanic Garden of Madrid who changed it to *Maurandya*. He is supposed to have referred to Maurandy's wife as '*Doña Catherina Pancratia Maurandy, wife of Don Agustín Juna, a learned lady, a sharer if not a leader in her husband's botanical labours.*'[130] A written description was first made in 1806 by Christiaan Hendrik Persoon

(1761-1836), a German mycologist.[131] Here, once again, it has been very difficult to find the true identity of Catherine Pancratia Maurandy. As well as the references above, the various accounts report she was a botany student at Cartagena around 1797;[132] assistant to her husband and the botanist Agustin Juan y Poveda (1770-1854), Director of the Cartagena Botanical Garden;[133-135] a Spanish botanist;[136] and a late 18th century Professor of Botany. [137] However, the description of her as a Professor of Botany is thought to be incorrect. *Maurandya scandens* (Cav.) Pers. is a climbing herbaceous perennial native to Mexico, with pink and white tubular flowers and untoothed leaves. It is grown as an ornamental plant in many parts of the world, and has often escaped from cultivation to become naturalized.

BOTANICAL NAME
Maurandya scandens

COMMON NAME
Creeping Gloxinia

FAMILY
Plantaginaceae

NATIVE OF MEXICO

Carolina Morren

According to one report, *Neoregelia carolinae* was named after Carolina, the wife of the editor of the magazine *Le Belgique Horticole*, Charles Jacques Edouard Morren (1833-1886), who was an authority on the Bromeliaceae. He was a Belgian botanist, Professor of Botany and Director of the

Neoregelia carolinae

BOTANICAL NAME
Neoregelia carolinae

COMMON NAME
Blushing bromeliad

FAMILY
Bromeliaceae

NATIVE OF BRAZIL

Botanical Garden of the University of Liège from 1857-1886[138] and was working on a monograph of the Bromeliaceae when he died unexpectedly at the age of 53 years.[139] His manuscripts and commissioned water-colour plates were sold to Kew Gardens by his widow Carolina shortly after his death. However, these seemingly authoritative reports are contradicted elsewhere where Charles Jacques Edouard Morren's wife is named as Euphemie Xhibitte who married Charles when he was 36 years old, in 1869.[140] Confusion reigns!

Neoregelia carolinae or Blushing Bromeliad is a species in the genus *Neoregelia*, noted for its centre which turns red when it is about to flower and from where the common name (Blushing) is derived.[141] This species is endemic to Brazil.

Juliana Schneider

Juliana Schneider is one of those women whose names appear in a plant species but only in the context of the '*wife of...*' The only information available about Juliana is that she was the first wife of Camillo Karl Schneider (1876-1951) then divorced from him before 1925, the year in which he married his second wife, Margot Haupt, who grew up in England. Juliana was born Juliana Kerber, but no dates have been found. There is, however, a Juliana Schneider with dates of 1874 to 1945 which match those of Camillo Schneider, but no further information is available to determine whether this is the person in question.

There is, however, much information about Juliana's husband, Camillo Karl Schneider who was an Austrian botanist and landscape architect who named *Berberis julianae* 'in compliment to his wife'.[142] A farmer's son, he was born in Saxony, and worked initially as a gardener in a tree nursery where his lifelong interest

Berberis julianae

in arboriculture began. Returning to Berlin to work in the City Parks Department, he assisted in editorial work for the periodical *Gartenwelt*, which led to his being employed as a landscape assistant in Darmstadt and Berlin.[143] In 1900, he moved to Vienna where his brother was a Professor of Zoology and Philosophy and where he worked as a research assistant in the botanical department of the Imperial-Royal Natural History Court Museum. In addition to his botanical studies, Camillo practiced as a freelance architect and writer, travelling extensively through Europe collecting specimens. In 1912 he published his book *Illustrated Handbook of Broad-leaved Trees*.[144] This had been issued in parts from 1904 to 1912. However, the manuscript of what should have been his *magnum opus*, a study of the genus *Berberis*, was destroyed in a bombing raid on Berlin in 1943.[145] In 1913, supported by the Austro-Hungarian Dendrological Society, he went to China to collect plants and seeds for the botanical garden at Pruhonitz. He then moved to Boston where he worked at the Arnold

BOTANICAL NAME
Berberis julianae

COMMON NAME
Wintergreen Barberry

FAMILY
Berberidaceae

NATIVE OF
CENTRAL CHINA

Arboretum alongside Charles Sprague Sargent, Alfred Rehder and E.H.Wilson until 1919, when he returned to Vienna as General Secretary at the Austrian Horticultural Society. Two years later, he moved to Berlin and continued to practice as a land-scape architect, redesigning gardens and parks in Germany.[146]

Juliana Lilac

His last book *Hecken im Garten* (*Hedges in the Garden*) was published in 1950. After serious illness, Camillo died of a stroke in 1851 in Berlin.[143]

Before their divorce, Camillo had named two plants after Juliana – *Berberis julianae*[142] and *Syringa julianae*.[147] *Berberis julianae* is native to western China and is a large evergreen shrub that is frequently planted in parks and gardens and used as hedging.[148] *Syringa julianae* (also known as *Syringa pubescens* subsp. *julianae*)[147] is an uncommon, attractive, weeping lilac with fragrant mauve flowers.

BOTANICAL NAME
Syringa julianae

COMMON NAME
Juliana Lilac

FAMILY
Oleaceae

NATIVE OF
SE EUROPE & E ASIA

78

References

1. *The Gardeners' Chronicle.* 1841-1985.

2. *Curtis's Botanical Magazine.* 1787.

3. Linnaeus, K. *Species Plantarum.* Sweden, 1753.

4. Biodiversity Library. www.biodiversitylibrary.org

5. Leese, B. *There She Grows*, Pixel Tweaks Publications, Ulverston, 2018

6. *Spring Grove House.* www.springgrovehouse.com/history.html

7. *Revesby Abbey.* www.revesbyestate.co.uk/heritage/

8. Harrison, C. *The Botanical Adventures of Joseph Banks*, Kew Publishing, London, 2020.

9. O'Brian, P. *Joseph Banks: A Life.* Harper Press, London, 1987.

10. Harrison, C. *Every Hill seemed to be Clothed with Trees of no Mean Size.* Kew Magazine, 101, 52-57, 2020.

11. *Dear Grandpa Pencil.* www.grandpapencil.net/austral/banks.htm

12. NASA Science, *James Cook and the Transit of Venus.*
www.science.nasa.gov/science-news/science-at-nasa/2004/28may_cook

13. Eaglen, R.J. *Sophia Banks and her British Hammered Coins.* British Museum, 2008.
www.britnumsoc.org/publications/Digital%20BNJ/pdfs/2008_BNJ_78_9.pdf

14. Leis, Arlene. *'A Little Old-China Mad': Lady Dorothea Banks (1758-1828) and Her Dairy at Spring Grove*: Journal for Eighteenth-Century Studies 40(2) July 2016. doi.org/10.1111/1754-0208.12410

15. Historic England: *Revesby Abbey.*
www.historicengland.org.uk/listing/the-list/list-entry/1000988

16. Blue Plaques: *23 Soho Square.*
www.english-heritage.org.uk/visit/blue-plaques/soho-square/

17. *Rosa banksiae* R. Br. ex Aiton, Hort. Kew. (ed. 2) 3, 258, 1811.

18. Young, L. *Lady Jane Franklin, the Woman who Fuelled 19ᵗʰ Century Polar Exploration.* Atlas Obscura 23 Feb. 2017.
www.atlasobscura.com/articles/cool-lady-jane-franklin-polar-exploration

19. Rawnsley, W.F. *The Life Diaries and Correspondence od Jane Lady Franklin (1792-1875)*. Cambridge Library Collection, Cambridge University Press, 1923.

20. *Eleanor Isabella Gell (Franklin)*. www.geni.com.

21. Franklin, J. *Narrative of a Journey to the Shores of the Polar Sea, in the Years 1819, 20, 21 and 22,* J.Murray, London.

22. Palin, M. *Erebus: The Story of a Ship*. Arrow Books, London, 2018.

23. Woodward, F. *Franklin, Lady Jane (1791-1875)*. Australian Dictionary of Biography. 1, 1966. MUP.

24. Worrall, S. *How the Discovery of Two Lost Ships Solved an Arctic Mystery*. National Geographic, 16 April, 2017.

25. Johnson, A. *Making an Exhibition of Herself: Lady Jane Franklin as Queen of the Tasmanian Extinction Narrative*. Journal of the Association for the Study of Australian Literature 14(3), 1-20, 2014.

26. Alexander, A. *The Ambition of Jane Franklin*. Allen and Unwin, London, 2013.

27. Arts Society of Tasmania artstas.clubexpress.com/

28. *Acradenia frankliniae* Kippist. Trees and Shrubs. www.onlinetreesandshrubsonline.org/articles/acradenia/acradenia-frankliniae/

29. Kippist, R. *Acradenia frankliniae* Kipp. Proc. Linn. Soc. London 2, 201, 1852.

30. Smith, V., *Common Ground: Who's Who in New Zealand Botanical Names*. New Plymouth, New Zealand, 2018.

31. Geneanet. www.geneanet.org.

32. J. M. C. (1886). *Edmond Boissier*. Botanical Gazette, 11(2), 39-40. www.jstor.org/stable/2994126

33. Boissier, Edmond, *Flora Orientalis*, Geneva, 1888.

34. *Omphalodes luciliae* Boiss. -- Diagn. Pl. Orient. ser. 1, 4, 41, 1844.

35. Vos, Anton. *Edmond Boissier, Gentleman Botanist*. Campus 120, Tete Chercheuse, University of Geneva, p.50, 2015. www.campus120_tetechercheuse_6TC.pdf

36. Armitage, A.M. *Herbaceous and Perennial Plants: A Treatise on their Identification, Culture and Garden Attributes*. Stipes Publishing, 2008.

37. Chionodoxa luciliae Boiss. Diagn. Pl. Orient. Ser, 1, 5, 61, 1844.

38. www.myheritage.com

39. Conservatoire et Jardin botaniques de la Ville de Genève - G. Geneva Herbarium – *Boissier's Flora Orientalis* (G-BOIS). Occurrence Dataset doi. org/10.15468/riran3 accessed via GBIF.

40. Fernand Jacquemond . *Sur l'herbier d'Edmond Boissier et la création d'un Herbier du Flora Orientalis* (G-BOIS) Arch.Sci. (2011) 64:5.

41. www.genealogie.dardel.info/ps01/ps01_095.html

42. Rutherford Hill, J. *Obituary Notice of the late James Edward Tierney Aitchison ND, CIE, FRS, Surgeon-Major, Bengal Army.* Transactions and Proceedings of the Botanical Society of Edinburgh, LXIII, 224-229, 1898.

43. www.ancestry.co.uk

44. Historic Environment Scotland. *Lothian bridge, Craigesk House including boundary wall and entrance gates* LB46966. Canmore. www.portal.histroicenvironment.scot/designation/LB46966

45. The Baron Courts of Prestoungrange and Dolphinstoun. The Dean Tavern – A Gothenburg Experiment. Ch.2 Newton Grange Village – the beginning. www.prestongrange .org.uk

46. Aitchison, J. *Flora of the Jhelum District of Punjab.* Botanical Journal of the Linnaean Society,8 (29), 55-75, 1864.

47. Aitchison, J. *Remarks on the Vegetation of the Islands of the Indus River.* J. Asiatic Soc. Calcutta, 34, 1865.

48. Aitchison, J. *Lahul, its Flora and Vegetable products &c.* From communications received from the Rev. Heinrich Jaeschke, of the Moravian Mission. *Botanical Journal of the Linnaean Society, 10, (42), 69, February 1868.*

49. Aitchison, J. *A catalogue of the plants of the Punjab and Siindh.* Taylor and Francis, 1869.

50. Aitcheson, J. *The Kuran Valley etc., Afghanistan. Rosa acae* Aitch. Journal of The Linnaean Society, Botany, 18, 54, 1880.

51. Murray, Peter. *No Hothouse Flower.* Irish Arts Review. Spring 2017.

52. Cockburn, P. *The Girl in the Painting.* Independent 27 June 2011.
www.independent.co.uk/arts-entrtainment

53. Mannion, N. *Lady Edith Blake, Irish Polyglot,Botanical Artist and Travel Writer.*
Irish Times, 5 September 2018.

54. The Lady Blake Collection: *Catalogue of Lady Edith Blake's Collection of
Drawings of Jamaican Lepidoptera and Plants.* Biodiversity Heritage Library OAI
Repository www.biodiversitylibrary.org/oai

55. Blake, Edith. *The Maroons of Jamaica'.*
The North American Review, 167, 558-568, 1898.

56. Ellwood, C.V. & Harvey, J.M.V. *The Lady Blake Collection: Catalogue of Lady
Edith Blake's Collection of Drawings of Jamaican Lepidoptera and Plants.* Bulletin of
the British Museum of Natural History 18 (2), 145-202, 29 Nov. 1990.

57. Harvard University Herbaria & Libraries. *Index of Botanists. Dunn, Stephen
Troyte.* Faculty of Arts and Sciences, Harvard University.
www.kiki.huh.harvard.edu/databases/botanists

58. Dunn, S.T. *New Chinese Plants. Bauhinia blakeana.*
Journal of Botany, British and Foreign, 46 (550), 325, 1908.

59. Lau, C.P.Y., Ramsden, L. & Saunders, R.M.K. *Hybrid origin of 'Bauhinia
blakeana' (Leguminosae: Caesalpinioideae), inferred using morphological,
reproductive, and molecular data.* American Journal of Botany, 1 March, 2005.

60. Hooker's Icones Plantarum. *Quercus edithae* Skan 1901. Hooker's Icones
Plantarum, 27 t: 2661, 1900.

61. Asher, Claire. *How a weird hybrid plant ended up on the flag of Hong Kong.*
BBC Earth,12 Dec. 2016.
www.bbc.com/earth/story/20161209-how-a-weird-hybrid-plant-ended-up-on-
the-flag-of-hong-kong

62. Anon. *Obituary John Matthew 1819-1869.* Minutes of the proceedings
of the Institution of Civil Engineers Part 2, vol. 30, 446-448, 1870 www.
icevirtuallibrary.com

63. Anon. *Obituary of William Hartree 1813-1859.* Minutes of the proceedings of the Institution of Civil Engineers vol. 19, 174-175, 1860. www.icevirtuallibrary.com

64. Anon. *Burford Lodge in Dorking, the seat of Sir Trevor Lawrence.* Country Life, 7th October 1899.

65. Anon. *Sir Trevor Lawrence (obit).* British Medical Journal 10 January1914, pp. 121-122.

66. *Sir Trevor Lawrence.* www.peoplepill.com

67. Reichenbach, H.G. *New Garden Plants. Aerides lawrenceae.* The Gardeners' Chronicle, 20, 460, 1883.

68. Anon. *New Aerides.* The Gardeners' Chronicle.508. 368-70, 1883.

69. *Aerides lawrenceae.* www.orchidspecies.com/aerlawrenciana.htm

70. Robeson, S.S. & Stroud, C.F. (K.H, Osborne ed.) *An Historical and Genealogical Account of Andrew Robeson of Scotland, New Jersey and Pennsylvania and his descendants from 1653-1916.* J.B. Lippincott Co., Philadelphia, 1916.

71. Champlin, K. *The Underground Railroad in Fall River.* Fall River Historical Society. Black History Month, 2017.

72. Beauregard, Burke and Franco. *Our Location.* www.bbflawoffices.com/about-us/our-location/

73. Find a Grave. *Zachariah Allen Jr.* www.findagrave.com/memorial/19066305/zachariah-allen

74. *Zachariah Allen. Fire and Explosion Hazards.* Proceedings of the 7th international Seminar 5-10 May, Providence, Rhode Island, 2013. www. rpsonline.com.sg/proceedings/9789810759360/html/zachariah.html

75. Emmanuel Church, Boston. www.emmanuelboston.org/tag/memorials/

76. V.B. Smocovitis. VB *Sargent Charles Sprague.* American National Biography.

77. Wilson, J. G. & Fiske, J., eds. (1900). 'Sargent, Paul Dudley' . *Appletons' Cyclopædia of American Biography.* New York: D. Appleton.

78. Michael Redman. Who was Nathanial Potter? Santa Barbara Independent July 6 2006 www.independent.com/2006/07/06/q-who-was-nathaniel-potter

79. Boston Herald. *Miss Alice Sargent Services Next Monday.*8 February, 14, 1946.

80.Coombes, A.J. A-Z of Plant Names. Hamlyn, London, 1994.

81. Wilson, E.H. *Lilium sargentiae.* Gardeners' Chronicle Ser. II, 51, 385, 1912.

82. Briggs R.W. *'Chinese' Wilson.* HMSO, London, 1993.

83. Musgrave T., Gardner C. & Musgrave W. *The Plant Hunters.* Ward Lock, London, 1998.

84. Wilson, E.H. *A Naturalist in Western China.* Cadogan Books, London, 1986.

85. Lyte C. *The Plant Hunters.* Orbis Publishing, London, 1983.

86. McLean, B. *A Pioneering Plantsman.* The Stationery Office, London, 1997.

87. President and Fellows of Harvard College. *Ernest Henry Wilson* (1879-1930) papers, 1896-1952: Guide. The Arnold Arboretum of Harvard University, 2009.

88. Howard, R.A. E.H. *Wilson as Botanist.* Arnoldia 40, 154-193, 1980.

89. Briggs RW. *'Chinese' Wilson.* HMSO, London, 1993.

90. Howard, R.A. E. H. *Wilson as Botanist.* Arnoldia 40, 102-138, 1980.

91. Sutton, S. B. *Charles Sprague Sargent and the Arnold Arboretum.* Harvard University Press, Cambridge, Massachusetts, 1970.

92. Wilson, E.H. *Letter to his mother,* 5 Feb. 1914.

93. Hemsley, W. *Berberis wilsoniae* Hemsl. Bulletin of Miscellaneous Information Kew, *151, 1906.*

94. *Rosa helenae* Rehder & E.H. Wilson. Plantae Wilsonianae; 1911, 310, 1915.

95. Smith, D. Forgotten *Travellers in the Land of the Blue Poppy.* www.duncanjdsmith.com, 2010.

96. Family Search. Florinda Norman Thompson. *www.ancestors.familysearch.org*

97. *Frank Kingdon-Ward.* www.french4tots.co.uk/Kingdon-Ward/plantlist.php

98. Lyte, C. Frank Kingdon-Ward, John Murray, London, 1989.

99. *Primula florindae* Kingdon-Ward, Notes Roy. Bot. Gard. Edinburgh 15(72), 84–85, 1926.

100. Find a Grave. *Racine Foster.* www.findagrave.com/memorial/16152758/eva-racine-foster

101. Racine, D. *Mulford Foster: A Man of Many Faces.* Journal of the Bromeliad Society 63(1), 16-74, 2013.

102. Barry, D. *Mulford B. Foster.* Journal of the Bromeliad Society 4(2), 15-19, 1954.

103. Foster, M.B. & Foster, R.S. *Orchids of the Tropics (Air Gardens Brazil.)* The Jacques Castell Press, Lancaster USA, 1954.

104. Piever, H. *Mulford and Other legends to Recall.* Bromeliad Society of San Francisco, 2-5, Oct. 2004.

105. Kew World Checklist of Selected Plant Families.

106. Martinelli, G., Magalhaes Vienta, M., Gonzales, *M. et al. Bromeliaceae da Mata Atlântica Brasileira* Rodriguesia 59(1), 209-258, 2008.

107. 'RHS Plant Selector *Aechmea racinae* AGM / RHS Gardening'. apps.rhs.org.uk.

108. *Aechmea racinae* L.B.Sm., Arq. Bot. Estado São Paulo 1: 56, 1941.

109. Marie Selby Botanical Gardens, Sarasota, Florida www.selby.org/botany/bromeliad-programs

110. Larsen, O.J. *Jean Rasmussen in Norway.* Yearbook of the Rhododendron, Camellia and Magnolia Group, 119-126, 2015.

111. Sealy J.R. *Lilium mackliniae* Sealy. Journal Royal Horticultural Society, London. 74, 349,1949.

112. Mao, A,A, & Gogoi, R. *Lilium mackliniae Sealy an endemic lily of north east India. Its distribution and status in the wild.* Indian Forester 139 (2), 170-104, 2001.

113. Macklin Kingdon-Ward, J. *My Hill So Strong.* Cape, London, 1952.

114. Carnaghan, C. *Jean Rasmussen.* Asian Affairs, 43:3, 546-547, 2012.

115. Siroi Lily. Edrom Nurseries. www.edrom-nurseries.co.uk

116. Pollak, O.B. Candour and Confidentiality: Textual Criticism. of Two Greek Letters on Anglo-Bunnese Relations, 1838. South East Asian Studies, 14 (2), September 1976.

117. *Dendrobium bensoniae.* Curtis's Botanical Magazine vol.93 (ser. 3 v.23) pl. 5679, 1867.

118. *Dendrobium bensoniae.* Bot. Zeitung (Berlin) 25, 230, 1867.

119. *Thunia bensoniae* Hook.f. Curtis's Botanical Magazine vol. 94 (ser.3 no.24). pl. 5694, 1868.

120. American Orchid Society. *Thunia.* www.aos.org

121. Botany Boy. A Rare Cane Orchid from Myanmar and Western Thailand. www.botanyboy.org

122. Travaldo Blogspot. *Dendrobium Care and Culture.* www.travaldo.blogspot. com

123. Dave's Garden. *Living Stones.* www.davesgarden.com

124. Charters M.L, *Plant Names L-O.* The Eponym Dictionary of Southern African Plants. www.calflora.net/southafrica/1L-O.html

125. *Women and Cacti* http://wiki256.pl/wom.html

126. *Biography of Franz Sales Erni.* S2A3 Biographical Database of Southern African Science. www.s2a3.org.za/bio/Biograph_final.php?serial=878)

127. *Lithops marthae* Loesch & Tischler. Succulenta (Netherlands) 18 (5), 74-76, May 1936.

128. *Lithops schwantesii* var. marthae (Loesch & Tischer) D.T.Cole. Madoqua ser. 1, 7, 35, 1973.

129. Lithops *schwantesii* Dinter. Sudwestofr. Lithopsart. 14, Dinter, 1928.

130. Bush, D. *A Spanish 'Blue-Stocking'.* Surinenglish. www.surinenglish.com/lifestyle

131. *Maurandya scandens* Pers. Syn. Pl. [Persoon] 2(1), 160, 1806.

132. Smith, A.W. *A Gardener's Handbook of Plant Names: their Meaning and Origin.* Dover Publications Inc. New York, 11, 1997.

133. José A. Mari Mut. *Ediciones Digitales, Aguadilla, Puerto Rico.* edicionesdigi-tales.info.12, 2017-19.

134. Novarum, aut. Riorum Plantarum Horti Reg. Botan. Matrit, Descrip-tionum Decades, 13, 22, 1797.

135. Ortega, Casimiro Gómez de Novarum, aut Rariorum Plantarum Horti Reg. Botan. Matrit. Descriptionum Decades (Decas prima, secunda, tertia, et quarta), 21, 1797.

136. Spencer, R. *Scrophularaceae*. Spencer, R. *Horticultural Flora of South-Eastern Australia. Vol. 4. Flowering Plants. Dicotyledons. Part 3. The Identification of Garden and Cultivated Plants,* University of New South Wales Press.15, 2002.

137. Quattrocchi, Umberto. *CRC World Dictionary of Plant Names vol. III*, CRC Press, London, 16, 2000.

138. Puccio, P. *Monaco Nature Encyclopaedia Discover the Biodiversity.* www.monaconatureencyclopedia.com/neoregelia-carolinae/?lang=en

139. Isley, P.T. *Tillandsia: The World's Most Unusual Air Plants. Vol. 1*, Botanical Press, New York, 1987.

140. *Charles Jacques Edouard Morren* (1833-1886). www.myheritage.com/names/Charles_Morren

141. Smith, L.B. *Neoregelia carolinae.* Contributions from the Gray Herbarium of Harvard University. 124, 9, 1939.

142. Sargent, Pl. Wilson. *Berberis julianae* C. K. Schneider. 1, 360, 1913.

143. Claas Heynowski, *Schneider, Camillo Karl*, in: Sächsische Biografie, ed. from the Institute for Saxon History and Folklore www.isgv.de/saebi/

144. Schneider, C.K. *Illustrated Handbook of Broadwood Trees*, Gustav Fischer, Jena, 1912.

145. Schneider, C. K. *Die Gattung 'Berberis'. Vorarbeiten für eine Monographie.* Bulletin de L'Herbier Boissier.Sér.2. Genève, V, 33, 1905.

146. Handel-Mazzetti, H. *Camillo Karl Schneider. A Botanical Pioneer in South West China.* Garden Magazine Illustrated Flora, 74, 27-29. 1951. www.paeo.de/h1/hand_maz/pioneer/ch43.html

147. *Syringa julianae* C.K.Schneid. Ill. Handb. Laubholzk. ii, 777, 1911.

148. *Berberis julianae.* Online Atlas of British and Irish Flora www.brc.ac.uk/plantatlas/berberis-julianae

CHAPTER THREE
ROYALTY

Queen Zenobia
Queen Charlotte
Maria Luisa of Parma
Empress Josephine
Queen Anna Paulowna
Franziska, Countess von Hardenberg
Queen Victoria
Queen Alexandra
Queen Natalie
Hortense van Nassau

ROYALTY

It is quite common for plants to be named after royalty, but these tend to be cultivated plants which do not feature in this book, for example, *Lobelia* 'Queen Victoria'; *Agapanthus* 'Queen Mum'; *Rosa* 'Queen Elizabeth' and *Rosa* 'Queen of Sweden'. To have a genus or species named after members of royal families is much rarer.

Ten members of royal families are featured in this chapter, seven of whom were queens, covering the years from 240AD when Queen Zenobia was born, to 1941 when Queen Natalie died. Although not strictly queens, Empress Josephine is also included, as is Countess von Hardenberg and Hortense van Nassau.

Many kings and emperors marry outside their own country, perhaps for political or financial reasons. This is well illustrated in this chapter where Queen Charlotte, the wife of the British King George III was German and the wife of King Edward VII was Danish. The wives of King Charles IV of Spain and also the King of Serbia were born in Italy, King Wilhelm II of the Netherlands's wife was Russian and Queen Victoria's husband was German.

Mystery surrounds the naming of both *Hardenbergia violacea* and *Hydrangea hortensia*. The former is said to have been named after

Franziska, Countess von Hardenberg about whom little is known except that she was Hungarian and had horticulturalists in her family. Similarly, *Hydrangea hortensia* could have been named after Hortensia van Nassau or Queen Hortensia, the daughter of Josephine de Beauharnais who was the wife of Napoleon I. Most accounts opt for the former.

The International Association for Plant Taxonomy (IAPT), located in Bratislava, oversees the naming of plants to ensure that there is no duplication or the provision of inappropriate names. Naming plants after royalty or even one's own husband or child is permitted: naming a plant after oneself is definitely not! Sometimes plants are named by the person who discovered them or alternatively by the person writing the first published description, who could be sitting in an office in a botanic garden remote from the location where the plant was first discovered! Until recently the description of a new plant genus or species had to be written in Latin. It was on 1 January 2012 that new rules were introduced to eliminate the language requirement and allow descriptions to be published electronically in online journals and books rather than in print only.[1] The new rules were designed to speed up the recognition process for new plant genera and species.

Of the 11 plants in this chapter, eight were named in the 19th century and only two in the 18th century. The plant missing from this list is *Hardenbergia* which was first given this name in the 20th century (1940) but had previously been named *Glycine* in 1781.

The naming of plants is a complex process, required to ensure that duplication of names does not occur and the information in a name is correct and provides appropriate knowledge of the plant's origins and position in the botanical world. The lives of the ten members of royal families now follow, ordered by date of birth, with Hortensia von Nassau last because her dates are not known.

Queen Zenobia (240-274)

Much has been written about Queen Zenobia but few people are aware of her significance and importance in ancient history. Her life and achievements were surely sufficient for her to have a genus named after her despite not having any recorded interest in plants! In summary, Zenobia was a third century Queen of Palmyra in Roman Syria who led a famous revolt against the Roman Empire. She was the second wife of King Septimius Odaenathus and became Queen of Palmyra after Odaenathus' death in 267. By 269, Zenobia had expanded the empire, conquered Egypt and expelled the Roman prefect, Tenagino Probus, who was beheaded after he led an attempt to recapture the territory. She ruled over Egypt until 274, when she was defeated and may have been taken as a hostage to Rome by Emperor Aurelian.[2]

Palmyra, the 'Pearl of the desert', which has recently come into prominence when it was destroyed by ISIS,[3] was, under the rule of Queen Zenobia, an oasis and stopping point on the Silk Road and a rebellious part of the Roman Empire, which, at that time was weakened by threats from Persia to the east and Europe to the west. In 260, the Emperor Valerian had been defeated and captured by the Persians. It was then that Zenobia decided to take advantage of the situation and expand her lands to the east. She had married Odaenathus, ruler of Palmyra, who wanted to establish himself to the east but failed when he was murdered in 267. Their son was too young to take over so Zenobia declared herself as Regent and,

BOTANICAL NAME
Zenobia speciosa
COMMON NAME
Honeycup
FAMILY
Ericaceae

NATIVE OF SE USA

Zenobia speciosa

with the current Roman Emperor being weak, declared Palmyra to be equal to Rome in importance. Zenobia gradually expanded her empire until it included Syria, present-day Turkey and Egypt. In 271 she declared her son to be Caesar (heir-apparent) but the more powerful Auralian, Roman Emperor at the time, took back many lands and put Palmyra under siege until it surrendered and Zenobia met her end. How this occurred is uncertain. She may have committed suicide to avoid capture or been taken to Rome and died there. Her origins are as uncertain as the circumstances surrounding her death, but she was well educated and could have been a member of a prominent Roman family.

The genus *Zenobia* is sometimes referred to as *Andromeda* and is a member of the family *Ericaceae* and is one of the lovliest *Ericaceae* shrubs originating in the bogs of the south-eastern USA. There are just three recognised species; *Z. speciosa,*[4-6] *Z. pulverulenta* and *Z. cassinefolia.* The genus was named by the Scottish botanist David Don (1799-1841) in 1834.[6] The picture is of *Zenobia pulverulenta*, the common English name of which is *Honeycup*. The flowers are fragrant, like large lilies-of-the-valley, with glaucous (bluish) young stems and leaves. They are hardy and tolerate almost full sun, but suffer in dry summers, thriving best in moist, peaty or leafy soil. They may be propagated by cuttings rather than by seeds.

Queen Charlotte (1744-1818)

As well as having a rather exotic looking flower, the Bird of Paradise has an unusual botanical name. The genus *Strelitzia* and the species *reginae* are named after Princess Charlotte of Mecklenburg-Strelitz who was the wife of King George III who ruled Britain from 1760 to 1820.[7] Charlotte married the King in 1761, a year after he was crowned, when she was just 17 years old and he was 22. She had only recently met George for the first time, but it is said their marriage was happy. They had 15 children and numerous grandchildren, one of whom was Queen Victoria. The portrait of Queen Charlotte, shown above, was painted by Sir Joshua Reynolds. Charlotte spent her early life in Germany in the Principality of Mecklenburg-Strelitz, and came to England speaking only German, though she quickly learned English. She was born Sophia Charlotte of Mecklenburg-Strelitz in 1744, and was the youngest daughter of Duke Charles Louis Frederick of Mecklenburg-Strelitz and Princess Elizabeth Albertina of Saxe-Hildburghausen. Mecklenburg-Strelitz was a small northern German Duchy and Charlotte was born and brought up at Untere Schloss (Lower Castle) in Mirow. The oldest of the King and Queen's 15 children was George, Prince of Wales, who became King George IV. He was born in 1762 when Charlotte was just 18 years old. He was quickly followed by Prince Frederick, Duke of York and Albany (b.1763), Prince William, Duke of Clarence (b.1765), Charlotte, Princess Royal (b.1766), Prince Edward, Duke of Kent (b.1766), Princess

Augusta Sophia (b.1768), Princess Elizabeth (b.1770), Prince Ernest, Duke of Cumberland (b.1771), Prince Augustus Frederick, Duke of Sussex (b.1773), Prince Adolphus, Duke of Cambridge (b.1774), Princess Mary, Duchess of Gloucester (b.1776), Princess Sophia (b.1777), Prince Octavius (b.1779), Prince Alfred (b.1880) and Princess Amelia (b.1783). Although St James's Palace was their official residence, the King purchased Buckingham House and the family moved there in 1762 and named it Buckingham Palace. Charlotte preferred it to their official residence and spent much of her time there. Until Queen Victoria, George III was the longest reigning monarch, and Charlotte was by his side, and a popular Queen during this time.[8] However, the reign was turbulent since it included the revolution in which Britain lost the American colonies, the union of Great Britain and Ireland in 1801, and the King's health was also of considerable concern.

However, *Strelitzia* was not named after Charlotte on account of her being the Queen, but because of her contribution to the advancement of Kew Gardens, where Kew Palace (known as the Dutch House) was one of her homes. She was an amateur botanist and lived at an exciting time when new plants were being brought back from expeditions across the British Empire by explorers such as Joseph Banks and Captain Cook. Native to the eastern coast of South Africa, *Strelitzia reginae* was introduced into Britain in 1773. It was one of the many exotic plants brought to England from South Africa by Francis Masson, a Scottish Botanist, and Captain Cook, on the HMS *Resolution*. *Strelitzia reginae* was one of more than 500 newly discovered species sent back. However, the plant had been well known in South Africa for many years and the person who was the first to discover it is unlikely to be known with any certainty.[9] The 'Authority' (i.e. the person who first described it) is variously attributed to Joseph Banks or William Aiton, a Scottish Botanist.[10]

The plant's common names, bird-of-paradise or crane flower refer to the exotic orange and blue flowers that look like the crests on birds' heads.[11]

Queen Charlotte and her husband were also patrons of music. Mozart performed for the Queen when he was eight years old and dedicated his Opus 3 to her in 1785. Charlotte also founded orphanages and in 1809 became Patron of the General Lying-in Hospital, which was subsequently renamed The Queen's Hospital, and is today The Queen Charlotte's and Chelsea Hospital, now located adjacent to Hammersmith Hospital.

Unfortunately for Charlotte, her husband became seriously mentally ill in later life, such that in 1810, their eldest son took over as Prince Regent until his father's death in 1820. Queen Charlotte was deeply affected by her husband's illness and suffered from depression, though she remained supportive of him to the end. After over 57 years as Queen, Charlotte died at Kew Palace in 1818, two years before her husband, and is buried in St. George's Chapel, Windsor Castle.[12] Many places around the world have been named after her, including Charlottetown on Prince Edward Island, Canada; Charlottesville, Virginia, USA and Charlotte, North Carolina, USA.[12]

BOTANICAL NAME
Strelitzia reginae

COMMON NAME
Bird of Paradise

FAMILY
Strelitziaceae

NATIVE OF SOUTH AFRICA

Strelitzia reginae

Maria Luisa of Parma (1751-1819)

The genus *Aloysia* is named after Luisa Maria Teresa Ana (known as Maria Luisa) of Parma who led a controversial life She was born in Parma, Italy and was the wife of King Charles IV of Spain (1748-1819), becoming Queen in 1788. Her father was Philip, Duke of Parma (1720-65) who was the fourth son of King Philip V of Spain. Her mother was Louise Elisabeth (1727-1759), the eldest daughter of King Louis XV of France. She died of smallpox at the age of 32 years leaving Maria Luisa and her brother and older sister.

In 1762, Maria Luisa became engaged to her cousin Charles, Prince of Asturias, and they were married in 1765 in Spain. She was said to be attractive at the time of her marriage, but after 24 pregnancies, of which 10 miscarried and only 6 children survived, she became prematurely aged. She was also intelligent, ambitious and dominant as well as being interested in music and art; indeed, she was known as a protector of artists, most notably Francisco Goya.

Although her relationship with her husband was good, Maria Luisa did tend to dominate him particularly since he was less interested in the affairs of the state than she was. She was unpopular during her reign, mainly because of her alleged love affairs, of which there was no evidence, and her support of pro-French policies that eventually were not favourable for Spain. Due to pressure from Napoleon I, her husband abdicated the throne of Spain in 1808, in favour of their son, Ferdinand VII. However, Napoleon I forced both Charles IV and Ferdinand VII to renounce their claims to the throne in favour of his brother Joseph. After the forced abdication, Maria Luisa and Charles IV lived as state prisoners of Napoleon in France, eventually in Marseille, where they stayed for four years. In 1812, they were allowed to settle under the protection of the Pope in Rome. After the fall of Napoleon in 1814, their son Ferdinand VII was reinstated to the Spanish throne. Maria Luisa and her husband both died in Italy in 1819, Maria reportedly from consumption.[13]

Nothing in Maria Luisa's life has so far indicated why the genus *Aloysia* was named after her.[14] The link is through her husband, Charles, who was a patron of the Real Jardin Botanico de Madrid (Royal Botanical Garden). The plant had already been received by the Botanical Garden from the French Botanist Philibert Commerson (1727-73) who accompanied Louis-Anton de Bougainville on his world circumnavigation in 1766-69. However,

it had earlier been named, but not published, by Casimiro Gómez Ortega and Antonio Palau y Verdera. The type specimen is known as *Aloysia citrodora* in Latin and 'Hierba de la Princesa' in Spanish, after Maria Luisa.[15,16]

Aloysia citrodora

BOTANICAL NAME
Aloysia citrodora

COMMON NAME
Lemon Verbena

FAMILY
Verbernaceae

NATIVE OF
SOUTH AMERICA

Aloysia is a member of the Verbernaceae (verbena) family and is native to northern Argentina and southern Bolivia. It smells strongly of lemon, hence its common name of lemon verbena, and it is used as a herb. It is also widely known as Lemon Beebrush because of the shape of its flower clusters. Its leaves are generally found in whorls of three and are lanceolate in shape (like a lance tapering to a point at the end) with flowers on spike-like branches or racemes forming an inflorescence. The plant has been used medicinally for disorders of the digestive system, as a sedative and as a tonic.[17]

Empress Josephine (1763-1814)

Marie Josèphe Rose Tascher de La Pagerie was born in Martinique to a wealthy white Creole family that owned a sugar plantation. She was a daughter of Joseph-Gaspard Tascher Seigneur de la Pagerie (1735-90), and his wife, Rose-Claire des Vergers de Sannois (1736-1807) who was from a wealthy Martinique family. Four months before Rose's birth (as she was known to her family), Martinique had been returned to the French from the British such that if she had been born later that year, she would have been a British citizen. Her father was not generous with money, leaving the family without the means of educating Rose in France which would have been the expectation for someone of her position.[18]

Rose's first marriage in 1779 was to Alexandre de Beauharnais (1760-1794), the step-son of her aunt Edmée Marquise de Beauharnais. He was guillotined in 1794 during the French Reign of Terror in the French Revolution (1789-99) and Rose was imprisoned in a former Carmelite convent. During her marriage, Alexandre was unfaithful and away for long periods. Nevertheless, they had two children, Eugène Rose de Beauharnais (1781-1824) and Hortense de Beauharnais (1783-1837) both of whom became step-children to Napoleon I, the second husband of their mother. Hortense later married Napoleon I's brother, Louis Bonaparte, who was King of Holland, making her the sister-in-law to her step-father, and the mother of Napoleon III, Emperor of France. All of these relationships served to make Josephine a key person in French history.

Moreover, through her son, Eugène, who married Princess Augusta of Bavaria, and their five daughters and two sons, Josephine was the great-grandmother of later Swedish and Danish kings and queens, as well as the last Queen of Greece. The reigning houses of Belgium, Norway and Luxembourg were also descended from her.[19]

In 1796 Rose married Napoleon I (1769-1821) and it was he who called her Josephine (her second name). In 1804 she was crowned Empress Josephine when Napoleon I became Emperor of France. They had no children, leading to their divorce in 1810 so that Napoleon could marry Marie Louise of Austria (1791-1847), with whom he had three children including a son who became Napoleon II of France. Despite their divorce, Josephine and Napoleon I remained on good terms.

Josephine's interest in plants was real and originated in the purchase of the mansion of Malmaison outside Paris in 1779, which became Josephine's own residence after her divorce. It is now a museum and can be visited.[19] Malmaison is well known for its menagerie and exotic gardens including a rose garden which was Josephine's special interest. She learnt about roses from her gardening staff and commissioned the artist Pierre-Joseph Redouté to paint the roses in the garden. His book, '*Les Roses*' (1817-20) contained paintings of about 80 of the roses growing at Malmaison.[20] Josephine procured her roses from an English company, Kennedy's, and also from Sir Joseph Banks at Kew. Her time was spent mainly in travelling and expanding her rose and other collections. *Hortensia*, or *Hydrangea macrophylla* is named after Josephine's daughter Hortensia, and also features in this book. Josephine died at Malmaison in 1814 at the age of just 51 years, from pneumonia, contracted after walking in her garden.

The Malmaison estate was inherited by Josephine's son, Prince Eugène and sold twice before being acquired by Napoleon III in 1861. In 1896 it was purchased by a philanthropist and donated to the state where it remains as a museum and gardens today.[21]

The Chilean Bellflower, *Lapageria rosea* was discovered and named after Josephine by two Spanish botanists undertaking an expedition to research the flora of Chile and Peru in 1777-1778 on behalf of King Carlos III of Spain.[22] The Botanists were Hipólito Ruiz López (1754 – 1816) and José Antonio Pavón (1754– 1840). There is only one species of *Lapageria* which is the National flower of Chile. It grows in the temperate rainforests of southern Chile and is not easy to grow. In its natural environment it is pollinated by hummingbirds. It is an evergreen climber with dark green alternate leathery leaves on stems which can be up to 10m long, with red or pink pendulous, bell-shaped flowers. The plants prefer well-drained soil and do not like to be dried out so may need watering every day. They require full or partial shade and flower between July and December.

BOTANICAL NAME
Lapageria rosea

COMMON NAME
Chilean Bellflower

FAMILY
Philesiaceae

NATIVE OF CHILE

Lapageria rosea

Queen Anna Paulowna (1795-1865)

Anna Paulowna Romanov, Grand Duchess of
Russia, was the wife of King Willem II of
the Netherlands (1792-1849). In Russia
she was known as Her Imperial Highness
Grand Duchess Anna Pavlovna of
Russia. Tsar Paul I of Russia and his
wife Sophia Dorothea of Württemberg
had ten children. Anna was their eighth
child and sixth daughter. She spent her
childhood in the summer residence of
the Romanovs, Tsarskoye Selo, with her
two brothers Nicholas and Michael. Anna
is said to have been well educated and good at
handicrafts and painting.

On 21 February 1816 Anna was married in the Winter Palace in
St. Petersburg to the Prince of Orange, the future King Willem II
of the Netherlands. Willem became a major general in the British
army and fought at the Battle of Waterloo in 1815, sustaining
a shoulder wound.[23] Anna took a very large dowry to the Low
Countries. Although she agreed to her children being brought up as
Catholic, she remained a member of the Russian Orthodox Church
for all of her life and missed her Russian heritage. Initially they
lived in Brussels, but a year after their marriage moved permanently
to The Hague in The Netherlands, which did not suit Anna. She
had a hard time adapting to her new environment, and continued
to hold on to the more formal ways of the Russian court and its
elaborate etiquette. The marriage was also stormy, not helped by
Willem's numerous affairs, but she continued to express her love
for him throughout their marriage. They had five children: Willem
(1817-1848) who became King William III of The Netherlands,
Sasha (1818-1848), Henry (1820-1879), Ernst (1822-1822) and
Wilhelmina (1824-1897).

In 1840 Willem I abdicated leaving the throne to his son, Willem II. The coronation took place in Amsterdam at a lavish ceremony and Anna became Queen of the Netherlands. She was not a popular Queen, being regarded as snobbish, but she did devote much of her life to funding 50 orphanages and a school to educate poor women in sewing, in line with her own crafting expertise. Willem II's reign was short; he died suddenly in 1849 at the age of 58 years after only nine years on the throne, and is buried in Delft. Anna was aged 55 when her husband died and withdrew from public life concentrating her efforts on her charity work.[24] There is no evidence that Anna had any botanical interests. She died in 1865 and was buried with her husband in Delft.

Paulownia tomentosa

BOTANICAL NAME
Paulownia tomentosa

COMMON NAME
Princess Tree

FAMILY
Scrophulariaceae

NATIVE OF CHINA

The genus *Paulownia* was named by the German botanist and physician Philipp Franz von Siebold (1796-1866) in honour of Anna. Siebold collected extensively in Japan but *Paulownia* is native to China. Joseph Gerhard Zuccarini (1797-1848) was another German botanist who worked extensively with Siebold.[25,26] The common name of the type species, *Paulownia tomentosa* is Royal Paulownia, (also known as Empress Tree, Princess Tree, and Foxglove Tree). These fast-growing trees have their own family, the Paulowniaceae.

Franziska, Countess von Hardenberg (1814-1871)

It has been remarkably difficult to find any information about Franziska Countess von Hardenberg, after whom *Hardenbergia* is named. According to Fred Harden, searching for his ancestors in 2003, '...(she) *was the sister of Baron Carl AA von Hugel. Franziska was apparently a '19th century Austrian patron of botany.' The 'apparently' is that's all I can find out about her. There is a visit recorded by Baron Charles von Hugel in 1834 and it turns out that this is the same man, Baron Charles (Carl, Karl) Alexander Anselm von Hügel (1795-1870) who was an 'Austrian soldier, diplomat, courtier, horticulturist and scholar.'* [27] If Franziska was indeed a '*patron of botany*' and her brother a '*horticulturalist and scholar*,' these are compelling reasons why the plant was named after her. This information also helps in narrowing down her dates to the 19th century. Since then, however, I uncovered further information indicating that Franziska was more likely to have been the sister-in-law and not the sister of Baron von Hugel (1795-1870). This Franziska was married to Gyorgy Andrassy (1797-1872), one of the founders of the Hungarian Academy of Sciences, and the brother of von Hugel's wife, Jozsefa Andrassy (1790-1868). Her name was Franziska Andrassy with dates of 1814-1871, in line with Baron von Hugel's. However, no mention of Hardenberg has been found which might indicate an association with Franziska, so the mystery persists. Franziska Andrassy was born Franziska von Koenigsegg-Aulendorf and had two sisters and a brother. She was a German noblewoman and married Gyorgy Andrassy, a Hungarian, in 1836. They had five children and she died in Vienna at the age of 56. The family home of the Andrassy's was to the east of Budapest in a wine growing region and the house is now a hotel. The family lived there until nationalisation after World War II.

Although best known for his travels in India in the 1830s, Franziska's brother-in-law, Baron Hugel, also collected plants while on an expedition to Australia in 1833.[28] In addition, he was the owner of a botanical garden in Hietzing, now a suburb of Vienna, and was known for introducing plants and flowers from New Holland (Australia) to Europe.[29] This information fits well with what is known about the plant genus *Hardenbergia* which is, indeed, from Australia.

Hardenbergia violacea

BOTANICAL NAME
Hardenbergia violacea

COMMON NAME
Sarsaperilla

FAMILY
Fabaceae

NATIVE OF AUSTRALIA

There are 17 named species of Hardenbergia but only three have been accepted.[30] One of the accepted names is *Hardenbergia violacea*, also known as the Happy Wanderer or Purple Vine Lilac. It is common throughout Australia particularly along the coast and in the mountains.[31] It was first described as *Glycine violacea* by the Dutch botanist George Voorhelm Schneevoogt.[32] Glycine is the genus of the related soy bean (Glycine max) and this plant was later combined with *Hardenbergia*, a name Bentham used in 1837 when describing *Hardenbergia ovata*.[33] The long, carrot-like root was reportedly used as a substitute for sarsaparilla by Australian aboriginal bushmen, so it is also known as Australian Sarsaparilla and False Sarsaparilla. *Hardenbergia* is an evergreen vine in the family Fabaceae, with stems up to 16 feet in length and flowers cascading down rather like *Wisteria*. It is hardy and requires well-drained soil.[34]

Queen Victoria (1819-1901)

Queen Victoria (Alexandrina Victoria) requires little introduction, even to residents in countries outside Britain and the Commonwealth.[35] Her family populated many of the thrones of Europe during the 19th century. She reigned from 1837 until her death in 1901 but was not born to be queen; she was the daughter of the fourth son of King George III and inherited the throne at the age of 18, after her father's three older brothers had all died without surviving children. Her father was Prince Edward, Duke of Kent and Strathearn, (1767 – 1820), the fifth child of King George III, and Victoria was his only child. He died when Victoria was just 8 months old.[36] Her mother was Victoria Saxe-Saalfield-Coburg (1786-1861), sister of Leopold, King of Belgium. Victoria also had a half-sister who was 12 years her senior, Princess Feodora, from her mother's first marriage to Emich Carl, Prince of Leiningen. When Princess Feodora was 6 years old, her father died. Her mother remarried Queen Victoria's father, the Duke of Kent, and moved from Germany to England for Victoria's birth.

In 1840, Victoria married her cousin, **Prince Albert** of Saxe-Coburg and Gotha (1819-1861), the son of her mother's brother. Royal etiquette at the time did not allow Albert to propose so she asked him to marry her. They had nine children before Albert died prematurely in 1861 at the age of 42 from typhoid after 21 years of marriage. Victoria's five daughters and four sons populated the kingdoms of Europe by marriage. Her eldest child, Princess Victoria (1840-1901) married Friedrich Wilhelm of Prussia, and their son became Kaiser Wilhelm II of Germany. Princess Alice (1843-78) married Prince Louis of Hesse, and their daughter Alexandra married Nicholas II the last Tsar of Russia, assassinated in 1917 in the Russian Revolution. Princess Helena (1846-1923) married Prince Christian of Schleswig-Holstein and Princess Louise (1848-1935) became the Duchess of Argyll. Finally, her sixth daughter, Princess Beatrice became Princess of Battenberg.[37]

The sons were equally well connected, Queen Victoria insisting they should marry into other royal families. Prince Albert Edward (1841-1910) became King Edward VII (1844-1910). Prince Alfred (1844-1900) married the Grand Duchess Maria, daughter of Tsar Alexander II of Russia and their older daughter Marie married the Crown Prince of Romania. Prince Arthur (1850-1942) married Princess Louise of Prussia. Prince Leopold (1853-84) died young of Haemophilia but was married for two years to Princess Helena of Waldeck-Pyrmont.[37] All of these alliances resulted in Victoria being known as 'The Grandmother of Europe.' After Albert's premature death in 1861, Victoria was devastated and remained in mourning for the rest of her life whilst ruling an empire.[38,39]

Her long reign of 63 years was a time of huge industrial, cultural, political, scientific, and military change coupled to the expansion of the British Empire. Furthermore, the Victorian era was known as the time when many exotic plants were brought back to Britain for the first time.[40,41] The industrial revolution in Britain in the 19th century was also responsible for a growing middle class which had been absent in earlier centuries. These wealthy industrialists had the means to build stove-houses or greenhouses at their mansions which enabled new tropical plants to thrive in an otherwise hostile climate. Such developments were assisted by the invention of the means to heat the stove-houses by the circulation of hot water, but these innovations were the preserve of the rich. In such circumstances it is no surprise that plants were named after Queen Victoria, although she is not recorded as having any particular interest in plants other than liking the violet as her favourite flower. Because of her great significance to Britain, two plants, rather than the usual one, have been selected here, a water lily and an agave.

The water lily *Victoria amazonica*[42] was first described in 1837 by John Lindley (1799 – 1865), the well-known English botanist and orchid expert. He acquired specimens brought back from British Guiana (now Guyana) by Robert Schomburgke, an explorer and botanist. The plant was named in honour of Queen Victoria when she ascended the British throne, and is the national flower of Guyana.

Victoria amazonica

Originally named *Victoria regia*,[43,44] there is still some dispute as to who was the first person to describe the plant and is, therefore, the recognised authority. Earlier in 1832, Eduard Poeppig had named the species *Euryale amazonica* and this name was acknowledged by James De Carle Sowerby, an English botanist, in his publication of 1850.[45] At the time, Lindley rejected this new name but it became generally known as *Victoria amazonica* in the 20th century. The contro-

BOTANICAL NAME
Victoria amazonica

COMMON NAME
Giant water lily

FAMILY
Nymphaeaceae

NATIVE OF SOUTH AMERICA

versy is set out in some detail by Donald Opitz and is a fascinating read.[46] Generally known as the giant water lily, the plant has spectacular leaves with a diameter of up to 3 metres which lie flat on the surface of the water. The flowers are white the first night they are open, become pink the second night and in the wild are pollinated by scarab beetles. They die after 48 hours. At botanical gardens such as Kew they tend to be hand-pollinated. On initial opening the flowers are female and their scent attracts beetles carrying pollen from other plants. After pollination the flower closes, trapping the beetles inside. The next day when the flower reopens it becomes male and the beetles transfer the pollen to other plants, so repeating the cycle.

The second plant selected and named for Queen Victoria is the *Agave victoria-reginae*, originally from Mexico and known as Queen Victoria's Agave. it was first described by Thomas Moore (1821-87) in the *Gardeners' Chronicle*, as follows: '*stemless, leaves thick, very rigid, deep green, roseate tuft, leaves with a dark spine....*' The plant was first seen in public at an International Exhibition in Cologne in September 1875 and was named with the Queen's permission.[47]

Agave victoria-reginae

BOTANICAL NAME
Agave victoria-reginae

COMMON NAME
Queen Victoria's Agave

FAMILY
Agavaceae

NATIVE OF MEXICO

Queen Alexandra (1844-1925)

Rheum alexandrae was named by the
Russian botanist Alexander Theodoro-
wicz Batalin (1847–1896) in honour
of Alexandra of Denmark who was
the wife of the British King Edward
VII.[48] Alexander Batalin was the
Chief Botanist and Director of
the Imperial Botanical Garden in St.
Petersburg. Although Alexandra had
links with Russia, expertise in botany
was not one of her known areas of interest.
After her marriage she and her husband were   the
first monarchs to choose Sandringham in Norfolk as one of their
residences. She did make changes to the garden there, but just why
this plant was named after her remains obscure, except that she was
'royalty' and very popular.

Alexandra was the youngest of the six children of King Christian
IX of Denmark (1818-1906) and Princess Louise Wilhelmine
Friederike Caroline Auguste Julia of Hesse-Kassel (1817 –1898).
They married in Copenhagen in 1842 and Christian became king
in 1863 following a succession crisis. One of Alexandra's sisters,
Dagmar, married the Emperor Alexander III of Russia in 1866,
where she was known as Maria Feodorovna. She was the mother
of the last Russian Emperor, Nicholas II who was assassinated in
1918 in Yekaterinburg during the Russian revolution. This was one
of Alexandra's Russian connections. The year 1863 was an important one for Alexandra: not only did she marry Edward, Prince of
Wales (1841-1910), known as Bertie, at the age of 18, but her father
took over the throne of Denmark and her brother became King of

Greece. She was Princess of Wales for 38 years until her husband became King Edward VII in 1901 on the death of Queen Victoria. Edward was 59 years old when he became king and reigned for nine years only, dying in 1910. From 1910 until her death in 1925, Alexandra was known as the Queen Mother or Queen Alexandra during the time that her son, George V, was king. Alexandra had six children, two of whom predeceased her. Her eldest child, Prince Albert, was born in 1864 and died in 1892 at the age of 28 while his father was still king. Alexandra's sixth child, Alexander John, born in 1871, died after two days. Her second son, George (1895-1936) became King George V on the death of Bertie in 1910. Alexandra had three daughters; Louise (1867-1931), Victoria (1867-1935 and Maud (1869-1938) who became Queen of Norway.[49]

So, what is known of Queen Alexandra's character and interests? She was well liked during the many years she spent as Princess of Wales and in her few years as Queen and then Queen Mother. She was said to have been dignified and charming in public and affectionate and fun loving in private. Her skills included wood carving and she was particularly interested in photography as well as dancing and ice skating. She was aware of her husband's many infidelities but remained loyal to him. Her relationship with her mother-in- law, Queen Victoria, was not always easy and she had also to bear the death of two of her sons, so despite her wealth and station in life, things were sometimes difficult for her. Nevertheless, she under-took the charity work expected of her with a particular interest in The London Hospital, frequently standing in for Queen Victoria, without rancour. While Princess of Wales, she and her husband had their London home at Marlborough House and, as mentioned, chose Sandringham in Norfolk as their country estate.[50,51]

Alexandra's health began to deteriorate around 1867 when she had a bout of rheumatic fever which left her with mobility problems, including a limp, and a propensity to deafness which grew worse with age. The death of her eldest son, Prince Albert from influenza in 1892 was also a severe setback for Alexandra. The end came in 1925 at Sandringham where, at the age of 80 years, she had a fatal heart attack. She is buried next to her husband in St. George's Chapel, Windsor.[49,52]

Rheum alexandrae, of the family Polygonaceae, is native to south-central China and Tibet and is closely related to the edible rhubarb (*Rheum* spp.). It is a striking plant with its tall head of overlapping cream-coloured bracts. The flowers are small and insignificant, appearing in May or June, and the leaves are borne in a rosette at the base of the plant. It is hardy and prefers full sun or partial shade and will grow in almost any soil type

BOTANICAL NAME
Rheum alexandrae

COMMON NAME
Alexandra's Rhubarb

FAMILY
Polygonaceae
NATIVE OF CHINA

Rheum alexandrae

Queen Natalie (1859-1941)

Queen Natalie of Serbia lived a turbulent life tinged with sadness. She was born Natalie Keşco in Florence in 1859, the first child of the Russian Colonel Piotri Ivanovich Kesco (1830-65) and Princess Pulcheria Sturdza of Moldavia (1831-74). Her parents had moved to Italy because the climate was milder for Natalie's mother who suffered from tuberculosis.[53] Natalie had two younger sisters; Maria (1861-1935) and Catherine, and a brother, John. Her father died at the age of 35 when she was 7, and her mother at 43, when she was 15.

As an orphan Natalie and her younger siblings were cared for by their maternal aunt, Princess Catherine Moruzi, granddaughter of the Prince of Moldova, Ioan Sturdza, and sister to Natalie's mother. Said to be a great beauty, Natalie was educated at a boarding school for the daughters of aristocratic families in Paris. In Belgrade in 1875, at the young age of 16, she married her second cousin Prince Milan Obrenovic IV of Serbia (1854-1901) who was 21.

Natalie's husband Milan had also experienced a difficult start in life. His parents divorced shortly after he was born and when he was seven years old his father was killed fighting the Turks. He was left under the care of his mother who showed little interest in him, and following an affair with the King of Romania, he was adopted by Prince Michael Obrenovic I of Serbia. However, in 1868 Prince Michael was assassinated, leaving Milan as his heir. A Regency was established until Milan, then 14 years old, could take over as head of the Principality of Serbia in 1875.

In 1882 Serbia became a kingdom with Milan and Natalie as King and Queen.[53] They had two sons but only one, born in 1876, survived. He became King Alexander I of Serbia ruling from 1889, when his father abdicated, to 1903 when he and his wife were assassinated during a military coup. Natalie's son lived for only 27 years.

Ramonda nathaliae

BOTANICAL NAME
Ramonda nathaliae

COMMON NAME
Nathalia Rock Plate or Natalie's Ramonda

FAMILY
Gesneriaceae

NATIVE OF THE BALKANS

The marriage of Natalie and Milan was turbulent as a consequence of Milan's unfaithfulness and their differing political views. They divorced but there was conflict with the church and she was exiled but eventually allowed back into the country. In 1893, Natalie and Milan were reconciled and asked the Serbian Government to revoke their divorce, which was done. Natalie's son Alexander wished to marry Draga Masin, his mother's former lady-in-waiting, but this was regarded as improper, resulting in the exiling of Natalie. She later became a Roman Catholic and a nun and spent the rest of her life in France where she died in 1941.[54]

As this book has illustrated, Central European countries have undergone numerous complex changes of name and allegiance over the last century or so. Moldavia (in English) or Moldova, which features in Natalie's family, was part of the Russian Empire from 1812. It returned to Romania in 1918 and was later occupied by the Russians in 1940. With the fall of the Communist regime, it became an independent country and gained independence in 1992.

Natalie's life featured no mention of plants, so why was *Ramonda nataliae* named after her? As it happened, the botanist who discovered the plant was a close friend of Natalie's husband, Milan. In 1873 Prince Milan Obrenović invited Dr Sava Petrović to his court and made him his personal physician. Sava Petrović (1839–1889) was one of the most important botanists in Serbia in the 19th century and also had qualifications in medicine. It was Milan who urged Petrović to investigate the flora around Niš which led to the discovery of *Ramonda nataliae* in 1882, later described by Josif Pančić in 1884.[55-57] Josif Pancic is regarded as the father of Serbian botany. The plant grows in Serbia, Macedonia and Greece, and is endemic to the Western Balkans. It is a member of the African Violet family, Gesneriaceae and is one of the rare, threatened and endemic plants of Europe, such that it is strictly protected in Serbia. The flower is considered a symbol of the Serbian Army's struggle during World War I. Natalie's Ramonda has predominantly round dark purple leaves and can grow up to 2 meters.

Hortense van Nassau

There is a mystery associated with the naming of *Hydrangea hortensia*. The *Hydrangea* itself had first been named in 1739 by the Dutch Botanist Jan Frederik Gronovius (1690-1762): meaning 'water pitcher' and referring to its shape.[58] Then in 1777, whilst in Japan, Carl Per Thunberg (1743-1828), a naturalist, named the *Hydrangea* and called it *Viburnum macrophylla*. In 1778 a specimen was then sent from China to Joseph Banks and he presented it to Kew. In 1792 it was reclassified into the genus *Hydrangea* and described as *Hydrangea hortensia*. It is now known as *Hydrangea macrophylla* 'Sir Joseph Banks.'[59]

Hydrangea itself is also known by the name *Hortensia*, given by the French botanist Philibert Commerson (1727-1773), and said, in some accounts to have been named in 1771 for Jeanne Baret (1740-1807), who later changed her name to Hortense. Commerson was a member of Louis-Antoine, Comte de Bougainville's round the world expedition between 1766-69, together with his lover Jeanne Baret, who disguised herself as a man in order to take part in the expedition, and, by accident becoming the first woman to circumnavigate the globe.[60] Bougainville (1729-1811) was a French explorer and admiral, after whom the exotic climbing plant *Bougainvillea* is named. Also present on the expedition was Charles Henri Nicolas Othon de Nassau-Siegen, a military adventurer, whose daughter, or possibly sister, was Hortensia van Nassau. One source says that Hortensia van Nassau was a '*tough and heroic lady who participated in an expedition around the world*' though at that time, open participation by a woman in such an expedition was very unlikely.[61] Another name suggested as the origin of Hortensia is that of Queen Hortense, the daughter of Josephine de Beauharnais and Napoleon I, though this explanation is considered to be less likely.[62] There are yet more explanations for the naming of *Hortensia*. One is that it derives from a translation of the Latin for *'from the garden.'* Thus, the Latin word 'hortus' means 'garden,' and Commerson found the Hydrangea in the garden of the King of Mauritius.[58] The most likely explanation for the name, however, is still regarded as commemorating Hortense van Nassau, about whom very little is known and there is no picture.

Hydrangea hortensia

BOTANICAL NAME
Hydrangea hortensia

COMMON NAME
Lacecap

FAMILY
Hydrangeaceae

NATIVE OF CHINA

Cultivars of *Hydrangea macrophylla*, are known as mopheads because they have a head of large petals all of a similar size, and are commonly found in gardens.[63] The plants are shrub-like in appearance with mid-green leaves while the flowers vary in colour depending on the pH of the soil in which they are grown. Pink flowers are common in alkaline soils, and blue, in acidic. The plants prefer moist but well-drained soil and full sun, although they also do well in partial shade.

References

1. International Code of Nomenclature for algae, fungi and plants (Melbourne Code). Regnum Vegetabile 154. Koeltz Scientific Books, 2012.

2. Hernandez de la Fuente, D. *Zenobia, the Rebel Queen who took on Rome.* National Geographic History Magazine www.nationalgeographic.com/history/magazine/2017/11-12/history-queen-zenobia-defied-rome/

3. Curry, A. *Here are the Ancient Sites ISIS has Damaged and Destroyed.* National Geographic. 1 Sept, 2015.

4. *Zenobia speciosa* (Michx.) D.Don Edinburgh New Philosophical Journal 17(33), 158, 1834.

5. Michaux, A. Flora Boreali-Americana 1: 256 in Latin, as *Andromeda speciosa,* 1803.

6. Don, D. *Zenobia.* Edinburgh New Philosophical Journal 17(33), 158, 1834.

7. Mabey, R. *The Flowering of Kew.* Century Hutchinson Ltd., London, 1988.

8. *King George III* www.royal.uk/queen-charlotte

9. Roberts, C. *Thought and Awe. What's in a Name 2014.* www.thoughtandawe.net/biology/botany/whats-in-a-name-2/

10. *Strelitzia reginae* Aiton, Hort. Kew. [W. Aiton] 1, 285, t. 2, 1789.

11. Oxford Plants 200: Plant 226 *Strelitzia reginae* Banks (Strelitziaceae) www.herbaria.plants.ox.ac.uk/bol/plants400/Profiles/st/Strelitzia

12. *Queen Charlotte* www.royal.uk/queen-charlotte

13. *Maria Luisa Teresa of Parma (1751–1819)* www.encyclopedia.com/women/encyclopedias-almanacs-transcripts-and-maps/maria-luisa-teresa-parma-1751-1819

14. *Aloysia.* www.en.wikipedia.org/wiki/Aloysia

15. Gómez Ortega, Casimiro & Palau y Verdera, Antonio. 1785. *Elementary course in theoretical and practical Botany, arranged for teaching at the Royal Botanical Garden of Madrid* . Madrid, Real Imp., 1788.

16. Palau y Verdera, A. *Aloysia citrodora Palau.* Parte Practica de Botanica 1. 767-771, 1784.

17. Kew Science. Plants of the World Online. *Aloysia* www.plantsofthe-worldonline.org/taxon/urn:lsid:ipni.org:names:1015993-1

18. Anne Theriault. *Queen of Infamy: Josephine Boneparte, from Martinique to Merveilleuse.* Long Reads. longreads.com/2019/03/28/queens-of-infamy-josephine-bonaparte-part-one/

19. Erickson, C. *Josephine: A Life of the Empress.* St. Martin's Press, London, 1999.

20. Redouté, Pierre Joseph. *Les Roses.* Imprimerie de Firmin Didot, Paris, 1817-24.

21. Musee National de Chateaux de Malmaison & Bois'Preau en.musees-nationaux-malmaison.fr/chateau-malmaison/c-life-malmaison

22. Ruiz, L.H. & Pavon, J.A. *Lapageria rosea* Fl. Peruv. 3, 65, 1802.

23. Kramer, K.C. *Slender Billy, William 11 of the Netherlands.* 6 December 2017. www.kyrackramer.com

24. *Princesses of Orange – Anna Pavlovna of Russia.* www.historyofroyalwomen.com

25. International Plant Names Index. *Paulownia Siebold & Zucc. 1835.* www.gbif.org/species

26. Siebold, P.F. *Paulownia.* Fl. Jap. 1, 25, 1835 [Dec 1835-Jan 1836].

27. Harden, F. *Another Country Diary.* 12 July 2003. www.thinktag.com/country/archive/country_diary072.htm

28. Anon. *Gardening Nirvana.* www.*gardeningnirvana*.com/tag/franziska-countess-von-hardenberg/

29. Wiesner, J. *Memorial Address. Charles von Hugel.* New Holland Journal: November 1833-October 1834 www.en.wikisource.org/wiki/Charles_von_H%C3%BCgel/Biographical_Sketch

30. The Plant List. *Hardenbergia.* www.theplantlist.org/1.1/browse/A/Leguminosae/Hardenbergia

31. Stearn, W.T. *Hardenbergia violacea* (Schneev.) Stearn The Journal of Botany 78, 70, 1940.

32. *Glycine violacea* Schneev., Type: Locus natalis. Nec de huius vero loco natali certiores sumus. Videtur vero ex eadem patria advenisse. [G. rubicunda Schneev.]. *Icones Plantarum Rariorum* 1, 29,1781.

33. Bentham, G: In Endlicher, S.L. et at.: Enumeratio Plantarum quas in Novae Hollandiae ora austrooccidentali ad Fluvium Cygnorum et in Sinu Regis Georgii collegil Carolus Liber Baro de Hugel. Fr. Beck, Vienna: 41, 1837.

34. Buchan, A. M. *Hardenbergia violacea (Fabaceae), Is it native in Tasmania?* Proceedings of the Royal Society of Tasmania, 128, 69, 1994.

35. BBC Teach. *Queen Victoria: The Woman who Redefined Britain's Monarchy* www.bbc.co.uk/teach/ks3-gcse-history-queen-victoria-monarchy/z73rnrd

36. Strachey, L. *Queen Victoria.* Mariner Books, London, 2002.

37. History Extra. *Who were Queen Victoria's Children?* www.historyextra.com/period/victorian/queen-victoria-prince-albert-children-who-names-sons-daughters-facts-motherhood-parents/

38. Baird, J. *Victoria: The Queen: an Intimate Biography of the Woman who Ruled an Empire.* Random House, London, 2016.

39. Wilson, A.N. *Victoria a Life.* Atlantic Books, London, 2015.

40. Aitkin, R. *Botanical Riches; Stories of Botanical Exploration.* Lund Humphries, London, 2008.

41. Lemmon, K. *The Golden Age of Plant Hunters.* Phoenix House, London 1968.

42. Plant Name Details. *Nymphaeaceae Victoria Lindl.* International Plant Name Index, 2005.

43. Lindley, J. 1837. *Notice of Victoria regia, a New Nymphaceous Plant. Victoria regia.* 16 October, 1837.

44. Anon. *Victoria regia.* Gardeners' Chronicle, 31 August, 1850.

45. Sowerby, J. de C. *On the Names of the Victorian Water Lily.* Annals and Magazine of Natural History, 26, 310, 1850.

46. Opitz, D. L. *The Sceptre of Her Pow'r': Nymphs, Nobility, and Nomenclature in Early Victorian Science.* The British Journal for the History of Science 47 (1) 67-94, 2014.

47. Moore, T. *New Garden Plants. Agave victoriae-reginae.* Gardeners' Chronicle. n.s., 4(2), 485, 1875.

48. *Rheum alexandrae* Batalin. Trudy Imp. S.-Peterburgsk. Bot. Sada xiii, 384, 1894.

49. Warnes, K. *Queen Alexandra. Windows to World History.* www.windowstoworldhistory.weebly.com/queen-alexandra-of-great-britain---queen-victorias-daughter-in-law-berties-patient-wife-and-her-own-person.html

50. Hough, R.A. *Edward and Alexandra: Their Private and Public Lives.* St. Martin's Press, 1st ed edition, 1993.

51. Ridley, Jane. *The Heir Apparent: A Life of Edward VII, the Playboy Prince.* Random House, 2013.

52. Battiscombe, G. *Queen Alexandra.* Constable First Printing Edition, 1969.

53. Flantzer S. Unofficial Royalty. *Natalija Keschko, Queen of Serbia* www.unofficialroyalty.com/natalija-keschko-queen-of-serbia/

54. Eilers Koenig, M. *Queen Natalie went to take the document.* 28.10.10. www.Royalmusingsblogspotcom.blogspot.com

55. *Ramonda nathaliae* Pančić & Petrovič . *Ramonda nathaliae Fl. Agr. Nyss. 574, 1882.*

56. Krüssmann, G. (October 1, 1986). *Manual of cultivated broad-leaved trees & shrubs.* Timber Press in cooperation with the American Horticultural Society.

57. Vasić, Olja. *Josif Pančić and the new Fora of Serbia'.* Flora Mediterranea. 23, 209–214, 1874.

58. *How the Hydrangea Got Its Name.* www.funnyhowflowersdothat. co.uk/how-hydrangea-got-its-name

59. *Hydrangea macrophylla.* The Joseph Banks Society. www.joseph-banks.org.uk/garden-plants/

60. Ridley, G. *The Discovery of Jeanne Baret: a Story of Science, the High seas and the First Woman to Circumnavigate the Globe.* Random House, New York, 2011.

61. Flower of the Month. *Hydrangea.* Florca Westland. www.florca. com/en/hydrangea:

62. *Hydrangea.* www.hydrangeaworld.com

63. *Hydrangea hortensia* Siebold. Nova Acta Phys.-Med. Acad. Caes. Leop.-Carol. Nat. Cur. 14(2), 688, 1829.

CHAPTER FOUR
GODDESSES

Artemis
Aspasia
Queen Cassiopeia
Danae
Diana
Dryads
Hebe
Laelia
Leucothea
Lycaste
Pandora
Pleione
Promeneia

GODDESSES

Thirteen mythological females have been identified who have had one or more plants named after them. They are shown in this chapter in alphabetical order and are represented in nine different plant families, the largest of which, with five representatives is the Orchidaceae (orchids). The Ericaceae family (heathers) has two representatives and the following are each represented once: Liliaceae (lilies), Ruscaceae (asparagus), Scrophulariaceae (figworts), Rosaceae (roses), Compositae (daisies) and Bignonaceae (trumpet creepers). Of the 13 genera, three are from South America, two each from Asia, Australia and North America and one each from New Zealand, Europe, China and Central America.

In the distant past it was traditional to name animals after gods and plants after goddesses.[1] Where the names of gods had been used for plants they were feminised in their botanical name. Because plants have beautiful flowers, the goddesses considered to be the most attractive tended to be selected for the names of newly discovered plants. In addition, John Lindley decreed that plant names should be both harmonious and non-descriptive and many botanists followed this injunction,[1] the names of goddesses fitting these requirements very well.

The gods and goddesses of ancient Greek and Roman mythology led complex and intertwined lives, often difficult to disentangle. There are many drawings and paintings depicting artists' impressions of goddesses' appearance but I have decided not to reproduce any of them here and would direct readers to the Internet to view them. In this chapter, only the picture of a key plant species associated with the named genus is given. Bernhardt's book '*Gods and Goddesses in the Garden*' provides an excellent introduction to this topic.[1]

Artemis

Artemis, the Greek equivalent of the Roman goddess Diana, has been described as the daughter of Zeus and Leto; King of the Gods, and a Titaness, respectively. Her twin brother was Apollo. She was the Greek goddess of the hunt; often being pictured carrying a bow and arrows. A virgin, she was also the goddess of wild animals and childbirth, and protector of young children. Despite this, Artemis joined with her twin brother Apollo to kill the children of Niobe who was married to a son of Zeus and had boasted that she had 14 children whereas Leto had only the twins. After killing Niobe's children, Artemis spent most of her time roaming the forests with her nymphs; hunting animals as well as protecting them.[1,2]

The Temple of Artemis was one of the seven wonders of the ancient world. It was built in Ephesus in Turkey in the 6th century BC and was also known as the Temple of Diana. Only the foundations now remain on the site: the other six wonders were: the Pyramids of Giza, the Hanging Gardens of Babylon, the Statue of Zeus, the Mausoleum at Halicarnassus, the Colossus of Rhodes and the Lighthouse of Alexandria.[3]

The genus *Artemisia* is in the daisy family Asteraceae (Compositeae), which contains 1598 species of which only 481 are accepted names.[4] The plant was first described by Carl Linnaeus in his famous book, *Species Plantarum* (1753).[5] The species pictured here is *Artemisia ludoviciana*, first named in 1818 by Thomas Nuttall (1786-1859), an English botanist who spent much of his life, from 1808 to 1841, conducting plant collecting expeditions in North America.[6,7] He was born in the village of Long Preston, near Settle in Yorkshire and spent some years as an apprentice printer in England. On his return to England in 1842, until his death in 1859, he lived at Nutgrove Hall in St Helens, Lancashire, which he had inherited from an uncle, on condition that he stay there for nine months each year.

However, he wrote, '*I prefer the wilds of America a thousand times over*' and returned once, for six months in 1847-48. [6]

Artemisia ludoviciana

Artemisia ludoviciana 'Valerie Finnis', the cultivar pictured here, is named after a female horticulturalist and photographer who specialised in alpine plants. Valerie Finnis received the Victoria Medal of Honour of the Royal Horticultural Society (RHS) in 1975 in recognition of her contributions to horticulture. She died in 2006 at the age of 81. This cultivar received the RHS's Award of Garden Merit (AGM) in 1993.

BOTANICAL NAME
Artemisia ludoviciana
'Valerie Finnis'

COMMON NAME
Mugwort

FAMILY
Asteraceae

NATIVE OF EUROPE

Plants belonging to the genus *Artemisia* can be shrubs, perennials or annuals; evergreen or deciduous, usually with grey, aromatic, often divided foliage and rather insignificant flower-heads. The cultivar 'Valerie Finnis' is an herbaceous perennial, forming clumps of lance-shaped, usually coarsely-toothed leaves, vividly white when young. The small, yellowish flowerheads are insignificant.[8] The plants prefer to grow in fertile, well-drained soil in full sun and are likely to die back in heavy, poorly-drained soil. Some are used medicinally, for example, in Chinese medicine and as a source of derivatives used in the treatment of malaria. The anti-malarial drug is known as Artemisinin and was discovered in 1972 by Tu Youyou, a female Chinese pharmaceutical chemist who, in 2015, shared the Nobel Prize in Physiology or Medicine for her discovery. The species *Artemisia absinthium*, or wormwood, is used to make absinthe, the first factory being set up in France in 1805 by Henri-Louis Pernod.[9]

Aspasia

In the 5th century B.C., Aspasia of Miletus (464-420approx.) was the most famous woman of Ancient Athens. She was neither a goddess nor as well-known as some of the other names in this chapter. However, I have decided to include her here rather than in one of the other chapters, since she fits none of them particularly well! She was the companion of Pericles who was an influential Greek statesman, orator and general in Athens during its 'Golden Age'; the peaceful years between the Persian and Peloponnesian wars (449 to 431 BC). Aspasia was not a citizen of Athens and, as such, was not allowed to marry an Athenian, although she lived with Pericles from around 445 to 429 BC. For this reason, their son, also named Pericles, could not take a citizen's role. However, eventually a special act allowed him to be made a citizen and he later became a military general. Women in ancient Greece had little power but Aspasia was an exception; she had influence, but became unpopular, and experienced discrimination because of her relationship with Pericles. She was accused of provoking a war with the city of Sparta and was charged with impiety but later acquitted.[10,11] Nevertheless, she had a supporter in the philosopher, Socrates, who credited her with eloquence, political influence and charm.

BOTANICAL NAME
Aspasia epidendroides

COMMON NAME
The Epidendrum-Like Aspasia

FAMILY
Orchidaceae

NATIVE OF CENTRAL
& SOUTH AMERICA

Aspasia epidendroides

The genus *Aspasia*, native of Central and South America, was named in 1830 by John Lindley (1799-1865), an English botanist and orchid expert.[12] The type species is *Aspasia epidendroides*, named in honour of Aspasia because of the flower's great beauty.[13,14] The description can be found in John Linley's work on orchidaceous plants.[12] The plants are epiphytes (i.e. found growing on other plants but not as parasites) and are found in lowland tropical forests from sea level to around 3,300 feet. The showy flowers are predominantly white, lavender, and brown, and from one and a half to three inches long. They are held on one or more inflorescences which can be up to 10 inches long.[15]

Queen Cassiopeia

Queen Cassiopeia, wife of King Cepheus of Ethiopia, was beautiful but arrogant and vain; characteristics that led to her downfall. Cassiopeia boasted that both she and her daughter Andromeda were more beautiful than all the Nerieds; the nymph-daughters of the sea god Nereus. This angered

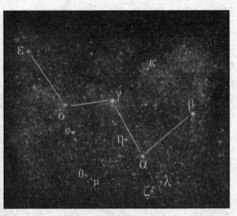

THE CONSTELLATION CASSIOPEIA

Poseidon, God of the Sea, who is said to have decided to flood the whole of the country of Ethiopia, or call upon the sea monster Cetus to destroy it. Whatever happened, Cepheus and Cassiopeia consulted a wise oracle in an attempt to save their kingdom, and were told that the only way to appease the sea gods was to sacrifice their daughter. They chained Andromeda to a rock at the sea's edge to await her fate at the hands of Cetus. But Perseus arrived in time, saved Andromeda, killed Cetus, and became her husband. Since Poseidon thought that Cassiopeia should not escape punishment, he placed her in the heavens tied to a chair in such a position that, as she circles the celestial pole on her throne, she is upside-down half the time, (matching the constellation Cassiopeia which appears as a W shape in the sky).[1]

The plant genus *Cassiope* was first described by the botanist David Don in 1834.[16] The Plant List identifies 38 species, of which 17 are accepted names.[17] David Don (1799-1841) was a Scottish botanist who became Professor of Botany at King's College, London as well as librarian at the Linnean Society in London.

His father, George Don Sr., was curator of the Edinburgh Botanic Garden. *Cassiope* are small shrubby plants in the family Ericaceae (heathers) and are native to northern temperate regions and the Arctic. They have scale-like leaves lying against the stems, and produce solitary bell-shaped flowers in late spring. Though hardy, the flowers can be damaged by late frosts. They are popular garden shrubs.[18]

Cassiope mertensiana

The species pictured here is Cassiope mertensiana, also known as white mountain heather and western moss heather. This heather is native to subalpine areas of western North America, from Alaska to the mountains of California. It is a small, branching shrub which forms patches along the ground and in rocky crevices. It was first named

BOTANICAL NAME
Cassiope mertensiana

COMMON NAME
Western Moss Heather

FAMILY
Ericaceae

NATIVE OF NORTHERN TEMPERATE REGIONS

as Andromeda mertensiana[19] in 1832 by August Gustav Heinrich von Bongard (1786-1839), a German botanist working in St. Petersburg but was renamed Cassiope mertensiana in 1834 by George Don Jr. (1898-1856), brother of David Don, mentioned above.

Danae

Danae's story is a complex one. She was the daughter and only child of King Akrisios and Queen Eurydice of Argos in Greece. The King longed for a male heir and asked the Oracle of Delphi for advice. He was told that he would never have a son and that he would one day be killed by his daughter's son. In order to avoid this catastrophic event, he locked Danae in an underground bronze chamber, but this was accessed by the King of the Gods, Zeus, who desired Danae. As a result, Danae gave birth to a son, Perseus, much to the dismay of her father. In order to avert the tragedy and prevent the Oracle's prophecy coming to pass, he put Danae and Perseus into a chest and sent them out to sea. However, the Gods intervened and saw them safely to the island of Seriphos where they were taken in by the brother of King Polydectes. The King wanted Danae to be his wife but she did not agree. The King only agreed not to marry her if Perseus brought him the head of the Gorgon, Medusa. Perseus achieved this using Athena's sword, Hermes' winged sandals and Hades' helmet of invisibility to decapitate the Gorgon. When Perseus returned, he discovered that his mother had fled to the Temple of Athena, and in anger he turned King Polydektes to stone using Medusa's head. He then travelled with Danae to Argos and claimed the throne of his grandfather, King Akrisios. On the way, Perseus went to the athletic games which were taking place at Larissa and by chance, accidently hit King Akrisios on the head with his javelin or discus, killing him, and so fulfilling the Oracle's prophecy.[1]

The genus *Danae* has just a single species, *Danae racemosa*.[21] Classification is complex but the genus *Danae* was first named by Friedrich Kasimir Medikus (1736-1808), a German botanist, in 1767.[22,23]

Danae racemosa

BOTANICAL NAME
Danae racemosa

COMMON NAME
Alexandrian Laurel

FAMILY
Asparagaceae

NATIVE OF
TURKEY & IRAN

The type specimen is *Danae gayae*[24] identified by Philip Barker-Webb (1793-1854) and Sabin Berthelot (1794-1880); English and French botanists, respectively, working in the Canary Islands. *Danae racemosa* is now the only accepted species in the genus *Danae*; none of the others is accepted, including D*anae androgyna* (L.) Webb & Berthel., D*anae gayae* Webb & Berthel., and *Danae laurus* Medik.[25,26]

Also known as Poet's Laurel, D*anae racemosa* is now in the family Asparagaceae but was previously assigned to both Ruscaceae and Liliaceae. It is a native of Turkey and Iran and the surrounding area. It prefers shade and should be kept out of full sun, producing a mass of dark green foliage. These 'leaves' are actually flattened stems known as phylloclades. The flowers are small and white, monoecious (hermaphrodite), and the berries round and red/orange in colour.[27]

Diana

According to Coombes, *Dianella* is the genus named after Diana, the Roman goddess of the hunt, known in Greek as Artemis (see Artemis/*Artemisia* in this volume).[18] As well as the huntress, she was also goddess of fertility, childbirth and the wild woodlands and is associated with the constellation of Ursa Major. She is also associated with fire festivals and her title, Vesta, indicates a perpetual holy fire. She had in attendance the sacrificial king, or king of the sacred rites who was required to pluck a branch of a certain tree (Virgil's Golden Bough) and kill his predecessor before taking up office. He then became a lover of the goddess and remained as such until he was murdered by his successor; a reminder of the cycle of birth, death and rebirth of nature. Diana was also considered to be the protector of the lower classes, especially slaves. Thus, the Ides (13th) of August, her festival at Rome and nearby Aricia, was a holiday for slaves. Another important centre for the worship of Diana was at Ephesus in Turkey, where the Temple of Artemis (or Diana) was one of the Seven Wonders of the World. It was built in the 6th century BC, but only the foundations remain on the site.[28] In Roman art, Diana usually appears as a huntress with a bow and arrow, accompanied by a hound or deer.[29]

BOTANICAL NAME
Dianella ensifolia

COMMON NAME
Flax Lily

FAMILY
Asparagaceae

NATIVE OF
SE ASIA & AUSTRALIA

Dianella ensifolia

The name *Dianella* was first formally published by Jean-Baptiste Lamarck in 1786 but this did not establish the name in a valid manner because Lamarck did not include a description of the new genus.[30] Antoine Laurent de Jussieu made it an accepted name in 1789 when he published a description in the first edition of his *Genera Plantarum*.[31] The type species for the genus is *Dianella ensata*,[32,33] now a synonym of *Dianella ensifolia*.[34] There are 100 species of Dianella, of which 41 are accepted.[35] *Dianella ensifolia* is also known as *Coryline ensifolia*, *Dracaena ensifolia* and *Dracaena ensata* of the family Asparagaceae. Its common name is flax lily. Members of the Asparagaceae are monocots with Dianella being an evergreen perennial with grass-like leaves growing from a branched, gradually spreading rhizome. It can grow up to 1.5 metres in height, spreading at the roots to form quite large clumps. The plant is sometimes gathered from the wild for use as a medicine, pesticide or dye, but is grown primarily for its ornamental nature.[36] The flowers have white or bluish-white petals and sepals, and bright yellow-orange anthers. Its berries are bright blue. The plant requires a sunny position in fertile well-drained soil and should be planted out in the spring to become established before winter.[37]

Dryads

The genus *Dryas,* currently in the family Rosaceae, is named after the Greek tree nymphs, the Dryads.[38] They were normally considered to be very shy creatures, except around the goddess Artemis who was known to be a friend to most nymphs. The name, Dryad, is derived from the Greek word for oak – *drys* – and they were origi-

Dryas octopetala

nally the spirits of oak trees, but the name was later applied to all tree nymphs. There are different groups of Dryads associated with different types of trees, for example, the Daphnaie are associated with laurel trees. Dryads were always female, attractive, and acted as guardians of trees or groves of trees. They were regarded as being mortal as well as

BOTANICAL NAME
Dryas octopetala

COMMON NAME
Mountain Avens

FAMILY
Rosaceae

**NATIVE OF NORTH AMERICA,
EUROPE & TEMPERATE ASIA**

minor goddesses. As such, most nymphs had some supernatural abilities and their lifespan, while not always immortal, was far longer than that of humans. Their powers were more limited, though, than the major goddesses.[39,40]

The genus *Dryas* was first named by Carl Linnaeus in 1753 in his *Species Plantarum.*[41] The genus is very similar to *Geum* with which it shares a page in *Species Plantarum*[42] as well as the common name Avens. The genus *Dryas* has 60 named species, of which 10 are accepted.[43]

139

Dryas differs from other members of the Rosaceae family in having more than the standard five petals: it has eight or more. They are native to the alpine and arctic areas of Europe, North America and Asia and are dwarf, evergreen shrubs with attractive, saucer-shaped flowers. The plants are tolerant and grow in unshaded areas such as tundra, fens and alpine areas. They are perfect for rockeries. The species *Dryas octopetala* (Holtasoley) is the national flower of Iceland.[44,45] It has oak-shaped leaves and flowers with eight petals, hence its name.[46] It is used as a herb to treat disorders of the mouth and throat.

Hebe

Hebe was the goddess of youth and the cupbearer of the gods who served ambrosia at the heavenly feast. Hebe exerted influence over eternal youth and had the ability to restore youth to mortals, a power that appears exclusive to her. She was also the patron goddess of young brides and an attendant of the goddess Aphrodite. Her parents were Zeus (the Roman God Jupiter) and his older sister Hera. Zeus was King of the Gods and lived on Mount Olympus. Hebe became the fourth wife of Heracles (the Roman God Hercules), with whom she had two sons. Heracles was a son of Zeus and his mortal wife, Alcmene, and the half-brother of Perseus.[1] Hera hated Heracles since he was the offspring of an illicit affair with Alcmene, which made him lose his mind, and kill his own first wife, Megara, and his children. In order to pay for his crimes, Heracles was required to carry out ten labours such that if he succeeded, he would be cleared of his sins and be granted immortality. This he accomplished.[47]

Hebe speciosa

The genus *Hebe* was first named by Philibert Commerçon (1748-1836) in 1789, and published in Antoine Laurent de Jussieu's volume *Genera Plantarum*; the first publication of a natural classification of flowering plants.[48]

BOTANICAL NAME
Hebe speciosa

COMMON NAME
Hebe

FAMILY
Plantaginaceae

NATIVE OF NEW ZEALAND

Commerçon was a French botanist who accompanied Admiral Louis Antoine de Bougainville on his round the world expedition in 1766-9.[49] *Hebe speciosa*,[50] the type species, was originally named *Veronica speciosa* which is still one of the plant's synonyms.[51] The latter two species were named by the Cunningham brothers, Richard (1793-1835) and Allan (1791-1839) who were English botanists working in Australia.[50,51] *Hebe* is native to New Zealand but is now found in many gardens worldwide. It is a member of the Plantaginaceae or plantain family with the common names: New Zealand Hebe, Showy Hebe and Showy-Speedwell. *Hebe speciosa* is an upright, evergreen, compact shrub that grows into a bun-shaped mound. It has glossy, green foliage and red/purple, short, spiky flowers from early summer to late autumn. The plants will tolerate some light frosts and will grow in any soil type.[52]

Laelia

The Roman goddess of the hearth, Vesta, was served by six 'Vestal Virgins' who had taken a vow of chastity. One such virgin was Laelia, whose duty it was to keep the sacred fire burning on her altar. If a Vestal Virgin failed in her duties, she was severely beaten and the punishment for loss of virginity was to be buried alive or have molten lead poured down her throat. Vesta's shrine was located in the Roman Forum where the virgins had to care for the shrine and its sacred objects and prepare food on Vesta's feast days. The Virgins

Laelia grandiflora

BOTANICAL NAME
Laelia grandiflora

COMMON NAME
Mayflower Orchid

FAMILY
Orchidaceae

NATIVE OF
CENTRAL AMERICA

were between six and ten years old when chosen by the chief priest and had to serve and remain chaste for 30 years. When released from service they were free to marry, but few did because it was considered unlucky. When the Christian Emperor Theodosius came to power, he disposed of pagan rituals and put out the sacred fire.53 In Greek legend, Hestia, daughter of Cronos and Rhea, was the equivalent of Vesta, being goddess of the hearth. She was the sister of Hera and Poseidon and was one of the twelve Olympian deities.1

In 1831, John Lindley was the first to identify the genus *Laelia*, which is native to Brazil.[54] He was an English botanist and gardener with a special interest in orchids who had an illustrious career in botany.

He was associated with the Royal Horticultural Society, after whom their library was named, held the chair of botany at University College, London, was a fellow of the Royal, Linnean and Geological Societies and author of numerous books including The *Genera and Species of Orchidaceous Plants*.[55] The type specimen is *Laelia grandiflora* (Lex.) Lindl., described in the same publication.[56] A synonym for this plant is *Laelia speciosa* (Kunth) Schltr.[57] *Laelia grandiflora* plants, known as Mayflower orchids are native to higher elevations in Mexico. They are drought resistant and tolerate cool to warm conditions. The flowers are fragrant with 3-4 flowers per inflorescence.

Leucothea

In Greek mythology, the plant *Leucothoe* was named after Princess Leucothea, the daughter of Orchamus, King of Babylonia, and his wife Eurynome.[58] Leucothea loved Apollo the sun god so he disguised himself as Leucothea's mother to gain entrance to her rooms, after which he changed his form back to his customary good looks which left Leucothea speechless and more inspired in her love. However, Clytia, sister to Leucothea, was jealous because she wanted Apollo for herself and told their father Orchamus what was happening, so betraying her sister's trust and confidence. Enraged, Orchamus ordered Leucothea to be buried alive and Apollo was unable to revive her. Apollo refused to forgive Clytia for betraying Leucothea, and she died slowly of a broken heart. Apollo changed her into an incense plant, either heliotrope or sunflower, which follows the sun every day.[1]

The genus *Leucothoe* was first described by David Don in 1834 [59] and in the same article he identified the type specimen as *Leucothoe axillaris* (Lam.) D. Don.[60] *Leucothoe* is a genus of about 50 species in the family Ericaceae (heathers), native to Asia, the Americas and Madagascar. Many species have the common name Doghobble. They are shrubs which can be deciduous or evergreen, depending on the species. The leaves are alternate and lanceolate in shape with bell-shaped flowers, usually white in colour, produced in racemes. Leucothoe plants, are moderately hardy. They prefer shade or partial shade and are not sun-lovers. Damp, acidic soil is their preference and they should not be allowed to dry out.[61]

BOTANICAL NAME
Leucothoe axillaris

COMMON NAME
Sierra Laurel

FAMILY
Ericaceae

NATIVE OF USA

Leucothoe axillaris 145

Lycaste

This orchid genus *Lycaste* was named after the mythological Lycaste, the beautiful daughter of King Priam and Queen Hecuba of Troy, and sister of Helen of Troy.[1]

Lycaste cruenta

It was first discovered by the English naturalist George Ure Skinner (1804-1867), who considered it to be the best find of his life which was spent searching Guatemala for beautiful, rare plants. He was particularly interested in orchids and introduced almost a hundred into the UK, one of which, *Lycaste skinneri,* is named after him. George Skinner was a trader in Guatemala City, willing to export anything, including animals as well as plants, all of which he sent to the Museum of Natural History in Manchester.

BOTANICAL NAME
Lycaste cruenta

COMMON NAME
The Blood Red Inner Lip
Lycaste

FAMILY
Ochidaceae

NATIVE OF
CENTRAL AMERICA

These were seen by James Bateman, a horticultural student, who asked Skinner to send him orchids, which he duly did. The first batch of orchids were exciting since they had not previously been seen in England. Bateman kindly asked John Lindley, the famous English botanist and orchidologist, to name one of them after Skinner – *Barkeria skinneri.*

In addition to his orchid activities Skinner also collected birds, some of which were sent to John Gould, a well-known bird painter. In one of the paintings in his book on humming birds, Gould included *Lycaste skinneri* Lindl. in honour of Skinner and thanked him in the acknowledgements.[62] A synonym for *Lycaste skinneri* is *Lycaste virginalis* (Scheidw.) Linden, the albino form of which is the national flower of Guatemala. The genus *Lycaste* has 117 species, 46 of which are accepted names, native to Central and South America.[63] It was first named by John Lindley in 1843.[64] The type species, *Lycaste cruenta* Lindl. was also described by John Lindley in the same publication.[65]

Being orchids, *Lycaste* flowers have three petals and three sepals and a wide variety of colours. *Lycaste cruenta*, pictured here, has a pleasant scent, as do many other species. They are native to the tropics and, as such, grow in areas with high humidity and cool to moderate temperatures. Indoors they grow best in bright filtered light with night temperatures of 55 to 60°F and daytime temperatures in the mid-80s or below. Flowers for many species and hybrids appear in late spring and early summer, though some are free flowering. Watering is important when the plants are almost dry and fertiliser can be used during the growing season.[66]

Pandora

In Greek mythology Pandora was the first mortal woman and was also responsible for releasing humanity's ills into the world, via her 'box.' Much to the anger of Zeus, King of the Gods, Prometheus, the God of Fire, had given the mortals special gifts including fire, so he decided to give them Pandora as an additional gift. In order to make her perfect, the gods gave her some extra divine characteristics: beauty from Venus, persuasion from Mercury, music from Apollo, voice from Hephaestus and pettiness from Hermes. Zeus gave Pandora to Prometheus's brother, Epimetheus and they married and had a daughter, Pyrrha. Epimetheus gave Pandora a box that she was forbidden ever to open, but she was curious and ultimately could not resist it. This released all the evil and mistrust into the world, including war, vice, toil and the need to work to live. Only 'hope' was left in the bottom of the box. This punishment allowed Zeus to feel compensated for the theft of fire and restored the division between the gods and humans.[1,67]

Pandorea jasminoides

BOTANICAL NAME
Pandorea jasminoides

COMMON NAME
Bower Plant

FAMILY
Bignoniaceae

NATIVE OF SE ASIA
& AUSTRALIA

The genus, *Pandorea* was named in 1840 by Edouard Spach, a French botanist, in his 14-volume publication, *Histoire Naturelle des Végétaux* (1834-48).[68] It comprises 30 named species, of which nine are accepted. The type species, pictured here, was originally named *Tecoma jasminoides* by

John Lindley in *Edwards's Botanical Register* in 1837[69] and was later renamed *Pandorea jasminoides* by Julius Schumann (1810-1868), a German botanist.[70] *Pandorea* is an evergreen, twining, climbing plant, native to the rainforests of Australia and South East Asia and requires a frost-free environment. *Pandorea jasminoides*, with the common name of Bower Plant, is an evergreen, twining climber favouring moist but well-drained soil. It has compound leaves made up of five to nine glossy, oval leaflets. The fragrant flowers are white with a dark pink centre.[71] They are borne in small clusters in spring and summer, and are tubular with spreading lobes 4-5cm across.

Pleione

Pleione played a central role in Greek mythology. She was an Oceanic nymph, the wife of the Titan, Atlas, and the mother of seven beautiful daughters; Maia, Electra, Taygete, Alcyone, Celaeno, Sterope and Merope, known collectively as the Pleiades. Pleione may have been one of the nymphs of the flocks who presided over the multiplication of the animals, because her name means 'to increase in number'. The parents of the Oceanic nymphs were the Titans; Oceanus and Tethys. Titans were the generation of gods preceding the Olympians. Zeus was himself an Olympian. Pleione's grandson, Hermes, as well as being messenger of the Gods, was the god of animal husbandry; he was a son of Zeus, and his mother the eldest of the Pleiades sisters, Maia.[72]

The genus *Pleione* was first named by the Scottish botanist David Don (1799-1841), in 1825. Don's father was curator at the Edinburgh Botanic Garden and David, himself, was Professor of Botany at King's College, London as well as librarian at the Linnean Society in London. Don was also librarian to the botanist Aylmer Bourke Lambert and compiled *Prodromus Florae Nepalensis*[73] for him, based on collections made by botanists at the Calcutta Botanic Garden. Of the numerous species of *Pleione*, the one selected here is *Pleione limprichtii,* also known as the Hardy Chinese Orchid, despite not being particularly frost resistant.[74] It is endemic to China, and is also found in the wild in northern Burma (Myanmar). The taxonomy of the genus *Pleione* is complex and open to dispute. The Plant List includes 88 species for the genus *Pleione*, of which 26 are accepted names,[75] whereas the World Checklist of Selected Plant Families lists 33 accepted names and 132 which are not accepted.[76] Readers might like to know that the *Pleione* website provides an interesting insight into the complexities of plant naming.[77]

The plants consist of a small pear-shaped pseudobulb which produces a single leaf, and the entire plant is no taller than 15 cm. The flowers, which appear in the spring, are deep pink in colour with rose red spotted lips. Plants are epiphytic, growing on the surface of another plant for physical support, but deriving moisture and nutrients from the air, rainwater or debris accumulating around them. They are frequently grown as houseplants and have gained the RHS Award of Garden Merit (AGM).[78]

Pleione limprichtii

BOTANICAL NAME
Pleione limprichtii

COMMON NAME
Hardy Chinese Orchid

FAMILY
Orchidaceae

NATIVE OF CHINA

Promeneia

The name *Promenaea* derives from Promeneia, the eldest priestess at the Greek Temple of Dodona, as described in the 4th century BC by Herodotus. The Oracle at Dodona is considered to be the oldest Oracle in Ancient Greece and second only in prestige to the Oracle at Delphi. It is situated in North West Greece in Eiprus, 1600 feet above sea level, east of Mount Tamaros. An Oracle is a gateway to the gods and to understanding of future events. Individuals would consult the priests and priestesses of the Oracle and wait for a response from the Gods. There are several explanations for how the Oracle at Dodona was established. Heroditus, an Ancient Greek historian, was told by three Dodonian priestesses, one of whom was Promeneia, that it was established by a black dove that flew from Thebes in Egypt and settled on an oak tree at Dodona. It spoke in a human voice to say that an Oracle to Zeus would be established at this location.[79] The three priestesses, Promeneia, Timarete and Nicandre guarded the Oracle from the 5th century B.C. and were known as the 'three doves.' Priestesses and priests in the sacred grove interpreted the rustling of the oak (or beech) leaves to determine the correct actions to be taken. It was an important religious sanctuary until the rise of Christianity during the Late Roman era.

BOTANICAL NAME
Promenaea xanthina

COMMON NAME
The Yellow Promenaea

FAMILY
Orchidaceae

NATIVE OF BRAZIL

Promenaea xanthina

The Oracle at Dodona was mostly used for private matters, unlike the Oracle at Delphi. which was consulted on matters of state.[80]

The genus *Prominaea* consists of 23 species, 18 accepted, and all restricted to Brazil.[81] The first description of the genus was provided by John Lindley in 1843.[82] The *Promenae*a orchids are compact plants with prominent pseudobulbs that often vary in shape, depending on the particular species. They are epiphytes and all produce an attractive display of flowers that are large in proportion to the size of the plant.[83] It is essential to provide plenty of water and high humidity during the growing season and the pots must never be allowed to dry out completely.[84] *Prominaea xanthina* is sometimes also known as *Promenaea citrina* because it bears one or two golden-yellow scented flowers per inflorescence.[83]

References

1. Bernhardt, P. *Gods and Goddesses in the garden: Greco-Roman mythology and the Scientific Names of Plants.* Rutgers University Press, 2008.

2. *Greek Gods and Goddesses.* www.greekgodsandgoddesses.net/goddesses/artemis/

3. *Inside History.* www.history.com/topics/ancient-history/sevens-wonders-of-the-ancient-world

4. *Artemisia.* The Plant List. www.theplantlist.org

5. *Artemisia* L. Species Plantarum 2, 845, 1753.

6. Nelson, J. *Thomas Nuttall.* Harvard Magazine, Mar-Jun 2015.

7. *Artemisia ludoviciana* Nutt. The Genera of North American Plants. Philadelphia, USA, 2 ,143, 1818.

8. *Artemisia ludoviciana* 'Valerie Finnis' www.rhs.org.uk

9. Drori, J. *The Incredible World of Plants.* Kew Magazine, 14, 36-43, 2021.

10. *Aspasia: mistress of Pericles.* Britannica. www.britannica.com/biography/Aspasia

11. *Aspasia of Miletus: the art of eloquence.* Ancient History Encyclopaedia.

12. Lindley. J. *Aspasia* Lindl., The Genera and Species of Orchidaceous Plants, 139, 1833.

13. Type species: *Aspasia epidendroides* Lindl. J. Bot. (Hooker) 1, 6. 1834.

14. *Aspasia of Miletus: the Art of Eloquence.* www.ancient.eu/article/80/aspasia-of-miletus-the-art-of-eloquence

15. The American Orchid Society. *Aspasia*
www.aos.org/orchids/orchids-a-to-z/letter-a/aspasia.aspx

16. Don, David. *An Attempt at a New Arrangement of the Ericaceæ*. Cassiope. The Edinburgh New Philosophical Journal. 1, 157–158, 1834.

17. *Cassiope*. The Plant List. www.theplantlist.org

18. Coombes A.J. *A-Z of Plant Names*. Chancellor Press, London, 1994.

19. *Andromeda mertensiana* Bong., Mém. Acad. Imp. Sci. St.-Péters-bourg, Sér. 6, Sci. Math. 2, 152, t. 5,1832.

20. *Cassiope mertensiana* (Bong.) G.Don Gen. Hist. of the Dichlamydeous Plants 3, 829, 1834.

21. Royal Horticultural Society. Plant Finder, 254, RHS, London 2018.

22. *Danae Medik*. Malv. Fam. 72, 1787.

23. *Danae Medik*. International Plant Names Index. www.ipni.org

24. *Danae gayae* Webb & Berthel., Hist. Nat. Iles Canaries 3(2; 3), 320, (1847).

25. *Danae*. World Checklist of Selected Plant Families. wcsp.science.kew.org/qsearch.do

26. *Danae racemosa* (L) Moench, Methodus , 170, 1794.

27. Farrow, R. November 2015 *Plant Profile. Danae racemosa*. University of Washington Botanic Garden. botanicgardens.uw.edu/about/blog/2015/11/03/november-2015-plant-profile-danae-racemosa/

28. *Inside History*. www.history.com/topics/ancient-history/sevens-won-ders-of-the-ancient-world

29. Encyclopaedia Britannica. *Diana*. www.britannica.com

30. *Jean-Baptiste Lamarck*. Encyclopédie Méthodique: Botanique. :276, 1786.

31. Antoine Laurent de Jussieu. *Dianella. Genera Plantarum,* Herrisant and Barrois, Paris, 41, 1789.

32. *Dianella ensata,* Plants of the World Online, Royal Botanic Gardens, Kew, powo.science.kew.org/taxon/urn:lsid:ipni. org:names:533827-1

33. *D. ensata* (Thunberg) R. J. F. Henderson, Taxon 26. 136. 9 Mar 1977.

34. *Dianella ensifolia ,*L. Redoute. Plants of the World Online, Royal Botanic Gardens, Kew.

35. *Dianella.* The Plant List. www.theplantlist.org

36. *Useful Tropical Plants* www.tropical.theferns.info

37. Royal Horticultural Society. *Cordyline.* RHS, London.

38. Greek Mythology. *Dryades and Oreiades.* www.theoi.com

39. Geller, Prof. *Who are the Dryads?* www.mythology.net

40. Greenberg, M. *Dryads: The Nymphs of the Trees.* www.mythology.net

41. Linnaeus, C. *Dryas* L. Species Plantarum,1, 501, 1753.

42. Linnaeus, C. *Geum rivale* L. Species Plantarum,1, 501, 1753.

43. The Plant List. *Dryas.* www.theplantlist.org

44. Flora of Iceland Elements: *Dryas octopetala, mountain avens.* www.iceland-nh.net

45. Linnaeus, C. *Dryas octopetala* L. Species Plantarum,1, 501, 1753.

46. The Royal Horticultural Society. *Dryas octopetala.* www.rhs.org.uk

47. *The Labours of Heracles.* www.perseus.tufts.edu/Herakles/labors.html

48. *Hebe* Comm. ex Juss., 1789. Gen. Pl. [Jussieu] 105, 1789.

49. Cook Museum Whitby. *Florilegium Travels: Bougainvillea spectabilis* www.cookmuseumwhitby.co.uk/the-museum/our-collections/our-florilegium-collection

50. *Hebe speciosa* (R.Cunn. ex A.Cunn.) Andersen, Trans. & Proc. New Zealand Inst. 56, 693, 1926.

51. *Veronica speciosa* R.Cunn. ex A.Cunn. Bot. Mag. 63, sub t. 3461, 1836.

52. *Hebe speciosa*. Royal Horticultural Society www.rhs.org.uk

53. Ancient history Encyclopaedia *Vestal Virgins*. www.ancient.eu/Vestal_Virgin/

54. Lindley, J. *Laelia* Lindl., The Genera and Species of Orchidaceous Plants. 115, 1831.

55. Stearn, W.T. *John Lindley 1799-1865: Gardener-Botanist and Pioneer Orchidologist*. Antique Collectors Club, London, 1999.

56. Lindley, J. *Laelia grandiflora* (La Llave & Lex) Lindl., The Genera and Species of Orchidaceous Plants. 115, 1831.

57. *Laelia grandiflora* (Lex.) Lindl. Plants of the World Online. www.powo.science.kew.org

58. GreekMythology. www.greekmythology.com/Other_Gods/Helios/helios.html

59. Don, D. *Leucothoe* D. Don, The Edinburgh New Philosophical Journal, 17, 159, 1834.

60. The Plant List *Leucothoe axillaris*. www.theplantlist.org

61. The Royal Horticultural Society. *Leucothoe*. www.rhs.org.uk

62. Brian Milligan. *George Skinner and his Orchids*.

www.oscov.asn.au/articles/george-skinner-and-his-orchids-by-brian-milligan/

63. *Lycaste*. The Plant List. www.theplantlist.org

64. Lindley, J. *Lycaste*. Lindl. Edwards's Bot. Reg. 29(Misc.), 16, 1843.

65. Lindley, J. *Lycaste cruenta* (Lindl.) Lindl. Edwards's Bot. Reg. 29(Misc.), 16, 1843.

66.House Plants Expert. *Lycaste Orchid.* www.houseplantsexpert.com/lycaste-orchid.html

67. Ancient History Encyclopaedia. *Pandora.* www.ancient.eu/Pandora

68. Spach, E. *Pandorea* Spach Hist. Nat. Vég. 9, 136, 1840.

69. Lindley, J. *Tecoma jasminoides.* Edwards's Botanical Register 23,2002, 1837.

70. Engler, H.G.A & Prantl, K.A.E. *Pandorea jasminoides* (Lindl.) K.Schum. Nat. Pflanzenfam. 4(3b), 230, 1894.

71. Royal Horticultural Society. *Pandorea* jasminoides. www.rhs.org.uk

72. Greek Legends and Myths. *Pleione in Greek Mythology.* www.greeklegendsandmyths.com/pleione.html

73. Don, D. *Prodromus florae nepalensis.* J. Gale, London, 1825.

74. *Pleione limprichtii* Schltr. Repert. Spec. Nov. Regni Veg. Beih. 12: 346 (1922). (Repertorium Specierum Novarum Regni Vegetabilis. Centralblatt für Sammlung und Veroffentlichung von Einzeldiagnosen neuer Pflanzen. Beihefte. [Edited by Friedrich Fedde]. Berlin).

75. The Plant List. *Pleione limprichtii* Schltr. www.theplantlist.org

76. World Checklist of Selected Plant Families (WCSP). *Pleione.* www.wcsp.science.kew.org

77. The Pleione Website. *Taxonomy.* www.pleione.info/taxonomy.html

78. Cribb, P & Butterfield, I. *The genus Pleione.* Royal Botanic Gardens Kew, 1999.

79. University of Warwick. *Sanctuary of Zeus at Dodona.* www.warwick.ac.uk/fac/arts/classics/intranets/students/modules/greekreligion/database/clukcw

80. Ancient History Encyclopaedia. *Dodona* www.ancient.eu/

81. The Plant List. *Prominaea* Lindl. www.theplantlist.org

82. Lindley, J. *Promenaea Lindl.* Edwards's Bot. Reg. 29(Misc.), 13, James Ridgway & Sons, London, 1843.

83. Schliefert, R. *The Genus Promenaea* The Orchid Societies Council of Victoria. www. oscov.asn.au

84. The American Orchid Society *Promenaea* www.aos.org/orchids/orchids-a-to-z/letter-p/promenaea.aspx

SUMMARY

SUMMARY

The aim of this chapter is to draw together the main findings of the earlier parts of this book. The four distinct groups of women who have had plants named after them, as identified from Coombs' book, 'A-Z of Plant Names'[1] are: plants-women; wives; royalty and goddesses. The plants-women were the subject of my earlier book There She Grows.[2] However, embarking on this venture, it soon became obvious that a second book would be required covering the other three groups, which, as I read more about them, became equally as fascinating as the plants-women.

In the end it took seven years to write the first book from start to final publication, largely because I took the decision to do a three-year BTEC course in horticulture, which, although it required attendance at college for just one day a week, included large amounts of homework such that the book received hardly a glance during that time. However, the project component of the course was important as a means of assessing the feasibility of my ideas and reinforced the notion that they were worth the first book, on plants-women, that eventually emerged.

This second volume on the other three groups, followed naturally from the first and did not take quite so much time.

In Chapter 1 there is some necessary repetition from the introduction to *There She Grows* to set the scene on how the individuals in this book have been selected. This is followed by a new section on how plants are named, beginning historically and leading to the genetically-based changes occurring today.

In Chapter 2, 16 women were identified who were best described as wives, although this did not mean they were without botanical or horticultural expertise – quite the reverse in some cases. The link between all of these wives is their husbands, who were either botanists or horticulturalists as a main occupation or, alternatively, more as a secondary occupation or hobby. These women, all of whom were wealthy, frequently took part in botanical explorations with their husbands and in many cases contributed as much. This group travelled extensively, frequently accompanying their husbands to overseas postings and took a full part in the life they found there. They were a diverse and interesting group with, in many cases, distinct lifestyles.

It is frequently forgotten, however, that many of the plant species 'discovered' by western explorers had been known for many years by the local communities in the areas where they were found. Efforts are now being made around the world to adjust narratives to recognise such omissions. For example, it is noticeable that in Kew's *'Our Manifesto for Change 2021-30'*,[3] one of the five priorities it sets out resolves to place more emphasis on the impact of plant exploration and its links to slavery.[4] The manifesto states *'We will move quickly to acknowledge and address any exploitative and racist legacies and develop a narrative around them.'*[3]

The diversity exhibited by the wives in Chapter 2 is mirrored, to a large extent, by the members of the royal families in Chapter 3. These women tended to marry members of royal families in countries other than their own. Examples are: The German-speaking Charlotte of Mecklenburg-Strelitz, the wife of the British King George III; Anna Paulowna of Russia, the wife of King Willem II of the Netherlands; and Alexandra of Denmark, the wife Britain's Edward VII. In some instances, such marriages were arranged, to increase the influence of royal families beyond their own countries.

PLANT HUNTING COUNTRYSIDE IN CHINA

WILD FLOWER MEADOW IN THE ALPS

Finally, in Chapter 4, the lives of 13 goddesses are described in all their complexity. Of course, having complex lifestyles is eminently possible for mythological figures who bear little resemblance to reality!

The wives, queens and goddesses profiled in this book are an eclectic selection; there are many others out there who could have been included if other sources of information had been accessed. However, it is to be hoped that this volume will go some way towards high-lighting the often-unsung contributions these women have made to botanical science. Their contribution will remain forever in the plants named after them.

THREE GODDESSES

References

1. Coombes, A. J. *A-Z of Plant Names*. Chancellor Press, London, 1994.

2. Leese, B. *There She Grows*, Pixel Tweaks Publications, Ulverston, 2018.

3. Royal Botanic Gardens Kew. *Our Manifesto for Change 2121-30*. Board of Trustees of the Botanic Gardens, Kew 2021.

4. Sanghera, S. *Empireland: How Imperialism Has Shaped Modern Britain*. Penguin Books, London, 2021.

APPENDICES

APPENDIX I

List of Plants featured in the book

Acradenia frankliniae Kippist 1852

Aechmea racineae L.B.Sm. 1941

Aerides lawrenciae Rchb. f. 1883

Agave victoria-reginae T.Moore 1875

Aloysia citrodora Palau 1784

Artemisia L. 1753

Artemisia vulgaris L. 1753

Artemisia ludoviciana Nutt. 1818

Aspasia Lindl. 1833

Aspasia epidendroides Lindl. 1834

Bauhinia blakeana Dunn 1908

Berberis julianae C. K. Schneid. 1913

Berberis wilsoniae Hemsl. 1906

Cassiope D. Don 1834

Cassiope mertensiana (Bong.) G.Don 1834

Chionodoxa luciliae Boiss. 1844

Danae Medik. 1787

Danae racemosa (L.) Moench. 1794

Dendrobium bensoniae Rchb.f 1867

Dianella Lam. ex. Juss. 1789

Dianella ensifolia (L.) Redoute 1802

Dryas L. 1753

Dryas octopetala L. 1753

Glycine violacea Schneev. 1781

Hardenbergia violacea (Schneev.) Stearn 1940

Hebe Comm. ex Juss. 1789

Hebe speciosa (R.Cunn. ex A.Cunn.) Andersen 1926

Hydrangea hortensia Siebold 1829

Laelia Lindl. 1831

Laelia grandiflora (La Llave & Lex) Lindl. 1831

Lamprococcus racinae (L.B.Sm.) L.B.Sm. & W.J. Kress 1989

Lapageria rosea Ruiz.&Pav. 1802

Leucothoe D. Don 1834

Leucothoe axillaris (Lam.) D.Don 1834

Lilium mackliniae Sealy 1949

Lilium sargentiae E.H.Wilson 1912

Lithops marthae Loesch & Tischler 1936

Lycaste Lindl. 1843

Lycaste cruenta (Lindl.) Lindl. 1843

Maurandya Ortega 1797

Maurandya scandens Pers. 1806

Neoregalia carolinae (Beer) L.B.Sm. 1939

Omphalodes luciliae Boiss. 1844

Pandorea Spach 1840

Pandorea jasminoides (Lindl.) K.Schum 1894

Paulownia Siebold & Zucc. 1835

Paulownia tomentosa Steud. 1841

Pleione D.Don 1825

Pleione limprichtii Schltr. 1922

Primula florindae Kingdon-Ward 1926

Promenaea Lindl. 1843

Promenaea xanthina (Lindl.) Lindl. 1843

Quercus edithae Skan 1901

Ramonda nathaliae Pančić & Petrovič 1882

Rheum alexandrae Batalin 1894

Rosa banksiae R. Br. ex Aiton 1811

Rosa ecae Aitch. 1880

Rosa helenae Rehder & E.H.Wilson 1915

Strelitzia reginae Banks ex Aiton 1789

Syringa julianae C.K.Schneid. 1911

Thunia bensoniae Hook.f. 1868

Victoria amazonica (Poepp.) J.C. Sowerby 1850

Victoria regina Lindl. 1837

Zenobia speciosa (Michx.) D.Don 1834

Zenobia pulverulenta (W. Bartram ex Willd.) Pollard 1895

Zenobia cassinefolia (Vent.) Pollard 1895

Note: the plants may have been renamed or have alternative names.

APPENDIX II

List of Authorities

The Authority is the person(s) who first published the name and description of the plant and follows the plant name in Appendix I. The list below identifies the names and dates of the Authorities.

A. Cunn.	Alan Cunningham 1791-1839
Aitch.	James Edward Tierney Aitcheson 1835-1898
Aiton	William Aiton 1731-1793
Andersen	Johannes Carl Andersen 1873–1962
Banks	Joseph Banks 1743-1820
Batalin	Alexander Theodorowicz Batalin 1847-1896
Boiss.	Pierre Edmond Boissier 1810–1885
Bong.	Gustav Heinrich von Bongard 1780-1839
C. K. Schneid.	Camillo Karl Schneider 1876-1951
Dunn	Stephen Troyte Dunn 1868-1938
D. Don	David Don 1799-1841
E.H.Wilson	Ernest Henry Wilson 1876-1930
G. Don	George Don 1798-1856
Hemsl.	William Hemsley 1843-1924
Hook.f.	Joseph Dalton Hooker 1817–1911
Juss.	Antoine Laurent de Jussieu 1748-1836
J.C.Sowerby	James De Carle Sowerby 1787-1871
Kingdon-Ward	Francis Kingdon-Ward 1885-1958
Kippist	Richard Kippist 1812–1882
K.Schum.	Karl Moritz Schumann 1851-1904
Kuntze	Otto Kuntze 1843-1907
L.	Carl Linnaeus 1707–1778

La Llave	Pablo de La Llave 1773–1833
Lam.	Jean-Baptiste Lamarck 1744–1829
L.B.Sm.	Lyman Bradford Smith 1904-97
Lex.	Juan José Martinez de Lexarza 1785–1824
Lindl.	John Lindley 1799–1865
Loesch	Alfred Loesch 1865-1945
Medik.	Friedrich Kasimir Medikus 1736–1808
Michx.	André Michaux(1746–1803
Moench	Conrad Moench 1744–180)
Nutt.	Thomas Nuttall 1786–185)
Ortega	Casimiro Gómez Ortega 1740–1818
Palau	Antonio Palau y Verdera 1734-1793
Pančić	Josif Pančić 1814–1888
Pav.	José Antonio Pavón Jiménez 1754–1844
Pers.	Christiaan Hendrik Persoon 1761–1836
Petrovič	Sava Petrovič 1839–1889
Poepp.	Eduard Friedrich Poeppig 1798–1868
Pollard	Charles Louis Pollard 1872–1945
R. Br.	Robert Brown 1773–1858
Rchb.f.	Heinrich Gustav.Reichenbach 1823-89
R.Cunn.	Richard Cunningham 1793-1839
Redouté	Pierre-Joseph Redouté 1759–1840
Rehder	Rehder 1863-1949
Ruiz.	Hipólito Ruiz López 1754–1815
Schneev.	George Voorhelm Schneevoogt 1775–1850
Schltr.	Rudolf Schlechter 1872–1925
Sealy	Joseph Robert Sealy 1907–2000
Siebold	Philipp Franz von Siebold 1796–1866
Skan	Alfred Skan 1870–1939
Spach	Édouard Spach 1801–1879

Stearn	William Thomas Stearn 1911–2001
Steud.	Ernst Gottlieb von Steudel 1783–1856
Tischler	Georg Friedrich Leopold Tischler 1878-1955
T.Moore	Thomas Moore 1821–1887
Vent.	Étienne Pierre Ventenat (1757–1808
W. Bartram	William Bartram 1739–1823
W.J.Kress	Walter John Emil Kress 1951-
Willd.	Carl Ludwig von Willdenow 1765–1812
Zucc.	Joseph Gerhard Zuccarini 1790–1848

APPENDIX III

List of plants in Chapter Introductions

The plants were photographed by the author in Yunnan, China in 2017.

1. *Aster souliei* Franch. 1896.	Asteraceae	Gang Ho Ba
2. *Stellaria chamaejasme* L. 1753.	Thymelaeaceae	Gang Ho Ba
3. *Incarvillea mairei* (H.Lev) Grierson 1961.	Paeoniaceae	Gang Ho Ba
4. *Androsace spinulifera* (Franch.) R. Knuth 1905.	Primulaceae	Gang Ho Ba
5. *Primula bulleyana* Forrest 1906	Primulaceae	Outstation
App. *Anemone demissa* Hook.f. & Thomson 1855	Ranunculaceae	Gang Ho Ba

PICTURE CREDITS

The author would like to thank the copyright holders for granting permission to reproduce the images illustrated. Every attempt has been made to trace accurate ownership of copyrighted images in this book. Any errors or omissions will be corrected in subsequent editions provided notification is sent to the publisher.

Chapter 3
Zenobia's Last Look at Palmyra: Herbert G. Schmaltz 1888, public domain; *Zenobia speciosa*: A.Barra WikiCommons CC BY-SA 4.0; Queen Charlotte: Sir Joshua Reynolds WikiCommons/public domain; *Strelitzia reginae*: B.Leese; Maria Luisa of Palma: Carlos Espinosa MoyaWikiCommons/public domain; *Aloysia citrodora*: H.Zell WikiCommons CC AS 3.0; Empress Josephine: Firmin Massot 1812 public domain; *Lapageria rosea*: Eric Hunt WikiCommons CC AS 3.0; Queen Anna Paulownia: Jan Baptist van der Huist 1837 WikiCommons/public domain; *Paulownia tomentosa*: Jean-Pol Grandmont WikiCommons CC AS 3.0; *Hardenbergia violacea*: Holger Casselmann WikiCommons CC AS 3.0; Queen Victoria: Alexander Bassano 1882 WikiCommons/public domain; *Agave victoria-reginae*: Brian Gratwicke WikiCommons CC AS 2.0; *Victoria amazonica*: B.Leese; Queen Alexandra: Alexander Bassano (1829-1913) WikiCommons/ public domain; *Rheum alexandrae*: B.Leese; Queen Natalie: 1875 WikiCommons/ public domain; *Ramonda nathaliae*: Francine Reiz WikiCommons CC BY-SA 3.0; *Hydrangea hortensia*: B.Leese.

Chapter 4
Artemisia ludoviciana 'Valerie Finnis': B.Leese; *Aspasia epidendroides*: Dalton Holland Baptista WikiCommons CC BY-SA 3.0; *Cassiope.mertensiana* var. Mertensiana: Walter Siegmund WikiCommons CC AS 2.0; The constellation Cassiopeia: Sadalsuud WikiCommons CC BY-SA 3.0; *Danae racemosa*: Dadonene89 WikiCommons CC SA 4.0; *Dianella ensifolia*: ritagu WikiCommons/public domain; *Dryas octopetala*: Anne Burgess WikiCommons CC SA 2.0; *Hebe speciosa*: B.Leese; *Laelia grandiflora*: WikiCommons CC BY-SA 3.0; *Leucothoe axillaris*: B.Leese; *Lycaste cruenta*: *www.peripatus.gen.nz* WikiCommons CC BY 2.0; *Pandorea* jasminoides: Forest & Kim Starr WikiCommons CC SA 3.0; *Pleione limprichtii*: B.Leese; *Promenaea xanthina*: Orchi WikiCommons CC SA 3.0.

Chapter 5
Plant hunting countryside in China: B.Leese; Wild flower meadow in the Alps: B.Leese; Three Goddesses: attributed to Giovanni Andrea Sirani (1610 1670) WikiCommons/public domain.

ACKNOWLEDGEMENTS

There are several people I am pleased to acknowledge for their support in the writing of this book. First, thanks must go to my husband, Henry, for his patience and persistence in the face of my frequent procrastination. There was always something else to occupy my time when, in reality, thinking – that sometimes most difficult of activities – was required! He has also spent much time editing and offering advice – not always accepted – but above all being my greatest source of encouragement. Thank you again!

Without the opportunity of a project as part of my horticulture course I suspect that this book would never have been written. To Shelagh Todd I express my grateful thanks, once again.

Russell Holden of Pixel Tweaks has been excellent in setting out my typed-up manuscript to look as attractive as it does. Many thanks, Russ. The cover illustration is by Sophie Holme who never fails to please with her excellent drawings – thank you, Sophie!

Thanks must also go to Cédric Basset who allowed me to use his own picture of *Rosa acae*. I am also grateful to Morgan Middlebrook of the Emmanuel Church, Boston for the picture of Mary Allen Sargent and family, to Larissa Glasser of The Arnold Arboretum for Ellen Ganderton Wilson, and to Trysha Long, Kiri Ross-Jones and Callum Duff of the Royal Botanic Gardens, Kew for pictures of Florinda Kingdon-Ward, James Aitchison and Jean Macklin.

This book has, once again, been written to give long overdue acknowledgement to the women within it. It has also been written for the female members of my family – Sarah, Louise and Mary – but not forgetting Henry, David and Matt. Perhaps my family will read some of it, who knows!

INDEX

A

Acer sikkimense 63
Acradenia frankliniae 15, 22, 38, 39
Aechmea racinae 66, 67
Aerides lawrenceae 15, 49, 51
Afghanistan 43, 44
Agave victoria-reginae 111
Aitchison, Eleanor Carmichael 27, 30, 42
Aitchison, James Edward Tierney 42
Aiton, William 96
Aiton, William Townsend 35
Aizoaceae 15, 73, 74
Alaska 134
Algae 21, 25
Aloysia citrodora 16, 99
Andrassy, Gyorgy 106
Andromeda 94, 133
Andromeda mertensiana 134
Aristotle 19
Arnold Arboretum 52, 54, 56, 57, 58, 59, 60, 61, 77
Artemis 125, 129, 137, 139
Artemisia 16, 129, 130, 137
Artemisia ludoviciana 129, 130
Aspasia 16, 125, 131, 132
Aspasia epidendroides 131, 132
Asteraceae 16, 129, 130
Athena 135
Australia 30, 33, 37, 107, 127, 137, 142, 148, 149
Austria 31, 102
A-Z of Plant Names 31, 163

B

Bahamas 30, 46
Banks, Joseph 30, 32, 34, 35, 96, 102, 118
Banks, Lady Dorothea 15, 27, 30, 32, 34, 35, 104
Barbey-Boissier, Caroline 41
Barbey, William 41
Baret, Jeanne 118
Barkeria skinneri 146
Bauhinia blakeana 15, 45, 47
Bauhinia variegata 47
Belgium 31, 102, 108
Benson, General Richard 71
Benson, Mrs 14, 15, 27, 31, 46, 71, 72
Berberidaceae 14, 15, 61, 77
Berberis julianae 15, 77, 78
Berberis wilsoniae 15, 58, 61
Berlin 77, 78
Berthelot, Sabin 136
Bignonaceae 127
Bird of Paradise 95, 97
Birmingham 17, 58, 59
Birmingham Botanical Gardens 59
Blake, Captain Henry 45
Blake, Edith 15, 27, 30, 45, 48
Boissier, Edmond 40, 41
Boissier, Lucile 14, 15, 27, 40, 41
Botanical Code 21, 22
Bougainvillea 118
Brassia lawrenciana 50
British Empire 17, 30, 46, 96, 109
British Museum 33, 46
Bromeliaceae 14, 15, 67, 75, 76
Brown, Robert 35
Burford Lodge 50
Burma 62, 71, 150

King Septimius Odaenathus 93
King Willem II 104, 165
King William III 104
Kippist, Richard 22, 39

L

Laelia 16, 125, 143, 144
Laelia grandiflora 16, 143, 144
Laelia speciosa 144
Lambert, Aylmer Bourke 150
Lapageria rosea 16, 103
Lawrence Gold Medal 50
Lawrence, Lady Elizabeth 27, 49
Lawrence, Louisa 50
Lawrence, Sir Trevor 50
Leucothea 16, 145
Leucothoe axillaris 16, 145
Liliaceae 14, 15, 41, 57, 70, 127,
    136
Lilium mackliniae 15, 62, 63, 68, 69
Lilium sargentiae 15, 56, 57
Lilium wardii 63
Lindley, John 110, 127, 132, 144,
    146, 147
Linnaeus, Carl 18, 19, 20, 21, **25,**
    79, 129, 139
Linnean Society 39, 133, 150
Lithops marthae 15, 73, 74
Lithops schwantesii 73
Lowell, Guy 54, 55
Luisa, Maria 16, 89, 98, 99
Lycaste 16, 125, 146, 147
Lycaste cruenta 16, 146, 147
Lycaste skinneri 146, 147
Lycaste virginalis 147

M

Macklin, Jean 15, 27, 30, 63, 67, 68
Madagascar 145
Madrid 74, 99

Malmaison 102, 103
Manipur 68, 69
Martinique 101
Massachusetts Horticultural Society
    61
Maurandy, AJ 31
Maurandya scandens 15, 74
Maurandy, Catherine 31
Mayflower orchids 144
Meconopsis 62, 63, 69
Meconopsis betonicifolia 63, 69
Mexico 65, 75, 111, 144
 Morren, Carolina 15, 27, 31, 75
Morren, Charles 31
Mount Siroi 68
Mrs. Aitcheson's Rose 44
Mrs Benson's Thunia 71, 72
Myanmar 71, 72, 86, 150
Myrtle Grove 48

N

Napoleon I 92, 98, 101, 102, 118
Napoleon II 102
Napoléon III 101
Neoregelia carolinae 15, 75, 76
Newbattle 42, 43, 44
Nicholas II 109, 112
Norway 69, 102, 113
Nuttall, Thomas 129

O

Ompholodes luciliae 15, 40, 41
Opitz, Donald 111
Orchidaceae 14, 15, 16, 49, 71, 72,
    127, 131, 143, 151, 152
Ortega, Casimiro Gómez 74, 99
Oslo 70

P

Palmyra 93, 94

Pandora 16, 125, 148
Pandorea jasminoides 16, 148, 149
Paphiopedilum lawrenceanum 51
Paris 17, 102, 115
Parma 89, 98
Paulowna, Anna 16, 89, 104, 165
Paulowniaceae 105
Paulownia tomentosa 16, 105
Pericles 131
Pernod, Henri-Louis 130
Philippines 49, 51
Pitcairnia feliciana 67
Plantaginaceae 15, 16, 75, 141, 142
Pleione 16, 62, 125, 150, 151
Pleione limprichtii 16, 150, 151
Polygonaceae 16, 114
Porden, Eleanor Anne 36
Primulaceae 15, 63
Primula florindae 15, 62, 63, 69
Prince Edward 95, 97, 108
Prince Milan Obrenović 117
Princess Catherine Moruzi 115
Princess Leucothea 145
Promeneia 125, 152
Prominaea xanthina 152

Q

Queen Alexandra 16, 89, 112, 113
Queen Anna Paulowna 16, 89, 104
Queen Cassiopeia 125, 133
Queen Charlotte 16, 89, 91, 95, 97
Queen Hortense 118
Queen Natalie 16, 91, 115
Queen of Palmyra 93
Queen Victoria 14, 16, 50, 89, 91,
   95, 96, 108, 109, 110, 111,
   113
Queen Zenobia 16, 89, 91, 93
Quercus blakei 47
Quercus edithae 47, 82

R

Ramonda nataliae 117
Rasmussen, Jean 68
Real Jardin Botanico de Madrid 99
Redoute, Pierre-Joseph 102
Rehder, Alfred 61, 78
Reichenbach, Heinrich Gustav 51,
   71
Revesby Abbey 32, 33, 34
Reynolds, Sir Joshua 95
Rheum alexandrae 112, 114
Rhododendron wardii 63
Rhododendron wilsonae 58
Robeson, Andrew 52, 53, 83
Rosa banksiae 15, 35
Rosaceae 14, 15, 16, 35, 44, 61,
   127, 139, 140
Rosa ecae 42, 44
Rosa helenae 15, 58, 61, 84
Rosa murielae 58
Royal Horticultural Society 50, 61,
   67, 69, 85, 130, 144, 151,
   155, 156, 157, 158
Russia 104, 109, 112, 165
Rutaceae 15, 39

S

Sandringham 112, 113, 114
Sargent, Charles Sprague 52, 54, 56,
   57, 59, 78
Sargent, Henrietta 55
Sargent, Mary Allen 15, 27, 52, 54,
   57
Sarsaparilla 107
Schneevoogt, George Voorhelm 107
Schneider, Camillo Karl 31, 76, 77
Schneider, Juliana 14, 15, 27, 31, 76
Scotland 18, 30, 42, 52
Scrophulariaceae 16, 105, 127
Sealy, Joseph Robert 68

Ingram Content Group UK Ltd.
Milton Keynes UK
UKHW020653230423
420577UK00012B/331